INCIDENT AT

DEVILS DEN

A TRUE STORY

BY

TERRY LOVELACE

COMPELLING PROOF OF ALIEN VISITATION

ALLEGED GOVERNMENT INVOLVEMENT AND

AN ALIEN IMPLANT

DISCOVERED ON A ROUTINE X-RAY

ISBN-13: 978-0-578-42032-5

ditor: George Verongos

TABLE OF CONTENTS

Preface

Devil's Den State Park in Northwestern Arkansas is a beautiful place. Folks who love the outdoors can appreciate its near perfection. But, beneath the scenic forests and limestone outcroppings there lies a mystery. People go missing from Devil's Den. A lot of people. Those missing souls go somewhere. The mystery is where?

Devil's Den is considered cursed ground by local Native Americans. Caddo and Cahinno tribes treat the land with measured deference and have done so as far back as anyone can recall. I wondered if Neolithic people felt uneasy when they walked these trails? In 1977, I couldn't shake the feeling someone was behind me. It was unnerving.

The Butterfield Trail that runs through the park is named after the Butterfield Stage Coach Line. The line operated from 1857 until hostilities between the States broke out in 1861. Horse-drawn coaches departed from hubs in St. Louis and Memphis, headed west to California. Their trek west took them through Devil's Den along the trail that bears its name. The trail wound through some of the most inhospitable land imaginable.

Devil's Den's history is rife with bloody skirmishes fought there during the civil war until the fighting ended in 1865. There is no written record of significant battles fought in Devil's Den during the war. The dense underbrush and limestone summits were ideal for snipers. It was difficult terrain for either side to hold and likely considered not important enough to devote men to the effort.

Up until the late 1880s, travelers through Devil's Den were subject to attack by opposing Native Americans who resented the trespass. There were lawless times when travel carried great risks. In more recent times, people just disappear.

In August 2017, Devil's Den claimed a 33-year-old man from Bartlesville, Oklahoma. His story struck a chord of empathy in me. Rodney's case is an eerie tale. I'll just touch on the highlights. During a hiking trip along the Butterfield Trail, Rodney Letterman became separated from friends when he decided to remain at the campsite and rest instead of continuing the hike. When the others returned, they found Rodney's cell phone. But Rodney

Letterman had vanished. All that was found was the cellphone left lying at their campsite. Like most of us, I bet Mr. Letterman's cellphone rarely ever left his hand or his pocket.

Letterman's hometown paper, the *Bartlesville Examiner,* stated that as of December 2017, "Two thousand five hundred acres were searched," and except for his cellphone, nothing has ever been found of Rodney Letterman. The Washington County Arkansas Sheriff, John Shuster, asked the public to help. He stated for the *Examiner*:

"All that we found was his cellphone … We'd like to hear from anyone who might now (sic) something about the case."

I promise to keep readers apprised of developments in Mr. Letterman's case on my Facebook page, Incident at Devil's Den. You may also check the Arkansas website at:

www.arkansasonline.com/news/2017/letterman.

Decades earlier, Devil's Den also proved to be unlucky for an eight-year-old girl from Pennsylvania. In June 1946, the Van Alst family from Pittsburgh camped at Devil's Den. The Van Alsts were a family of five. There was eight-year-old Kathryn, her parents, and two brothers.

The precise details surrounding the day of her disappearance hav been lost to time. It's known that Kathryn vanished from the family' campsite and a desperate search effort began. Details are scant, but Kathryn' disappearance was documented in the Van Alst family's hometow newspaper, the *Pittsburgh Press*.

In a story that ran June 24, 1946, the *Press* stated that after a week i the forest Kathryn was found. Her rescuer was identified as a search voluntee from the University of Arkansas, "19-year-old Chadwick." Chadwick wa quoted as saying, "I called Kathryn's name and she walked out of a small cav dressed in her bathing suit and announced calmly, 'here I am.'"

In David Paulides's book *Missing 411*, he tells how Kathryn wa found seven air miles and 600 feet elevation from the campsite. To reach th point would have required a twenty-mile trek on zigzagging trails and rough terrain. Without shoes. The area where Chadwick found her had been previously searched. Twice. Once by air and again by volunteers.

What struck me as odd were quotes made in the *Press* by her rescuer, Chadwick, and Kathryn's mother. The *Press* quoted "Chadwick" as describing Kathryn's demeanor as, "eerily calm."

When asked by the *Press,* Kathryn's mother described her daughter's mood as, "utterly serene."

The phrases "eerily calm" and "utterly serene" just seem out of context. It's puzzling to me.

Despite the absence of potable water anywhere near the site, Kathryn was found well hydrated and had not lost weight. She told her rescuers she could not recall how she got lost or what happened to her.

I tried to locate Chadwick through the University of Arkansas enrollment records and graduation records. Since it's unclear if Chadwick was a first or last name, it was difficult. The college also pointed out it may have been a student named Chadwick who chose to be called "Chad." If my name were Chadwick, I'd prefer Chad.

I tried to locate Kathryn Van Alst who would now be seventy plus years of age. I was unsuccessful. It's an opportunity lost that she was never interviewed as an adult. I've thought about Kathryn often and wondered if Devil's Den plagued Kathryn's sleep the way it's plagued mine for a half-century.

I'm grateful to have survived Devil's Den. It cost my friend his life.

Introduction

I want to be clear from the start. I'm not on a mission to change your mind about the topic of UFOs or the existence of alien life. There are people like myself who've had experiences, and most spend an entire lifetime and never see a thing. I've never been a fan of science fiction. I don't read books about UFOs or any related topics. They disturb my sleep the way explicit crime novels keep my wife awake at night.

The genesis of this book is an event that occurred in 1977. While camping at a state park, a friend and I encountered an enormous UFO. It was triangular-shaped, and each side was approximately a city block in length. I'd estimate it was five stories tall with a matte black finish. All three corners were brilliantly lit from the bottom to the top with flashing multicolored lights.

It emitted a low drone. The noise was what you'd experience standing next to a very large piece of equipment like a diesel train engine. It was a bass one that reverberated in your chest.

I'm a retired lawyer who spent many years in state government as a prosecutor and as an assistant attorney general. During my professional career, I didn't disclose these things for fear of losing my job and standing in he legal community. So, my wife and I kept these experiences to ourselves or 41 years. I planned to take the story to my grave.

Until 2012, when an anomalous piece of metal, found in my knee, hanged things dramatically. That fingernail-sized piece of metal was the ipping point for me. It was the catalyst to write this book, speak publicly, and ake a full and candid disclosure of everything that's happened. My xperiences with UFOs stretch back to my early childhood.

Why was I singled out for these four or five experiences over the span f a lifetime? I think it's because I was tagged. Like an animal on the erengeti Plains of Africa.

This unexpected discovery motivated me to tell the world what appened to me nearly fifty years ago. It's difficult for me to accept that I ave a metallic "thing" in my leg that medical science can't explain. The idea at nonhuman entities seized me and laid hands upon me makes my skin crawl. What happened to me may well have happened to you or someone you love. That "bad dream" you once had that seemed so real may not have been a nightmare. It may have been a memory.

If intelligent extraterrestrial beings are out there, then where are they? The United States Government steadfastly asserts that there's no proof of alien life anywhere on Earth, or elsewhere in the universe. There's a new acronym to replace UFO. It's now UAP for, "Unknown Aerial Phenomena" in government circles. Whether UFOs or UAPs, the government claims it isn't interested.

The United States Government has no department or agency responsible for investigating UFO sightings. Citizens who wish to report a UFO are referred to their local law enforcement agency. Unless there's a crash involved, then it's an entirely different matter.

Imagine, on your drive home from work one afternoon, a silvery disc sails right over your car and abruptly stops in front of you. It's 50 feet, or less overhead and you have a crystal-clear view. You pull over and watch. You're astounded! You wonder, "What is this thing?" Your mind races with possible explanations eliminating them one by one. This thing is big too. You'd estimate it to be 90 feet in diameter, bright, and shiny. Your peripheral vision notices that it casts an elliptical shadow to your left, consistent with the placement of the afternoon sun.

A couple of other cars have also pulled over. Other motorists are witnessing this too, so it can't be a product of your imagination. Some peopl have opened their car doors and are standing outside for a better look Everyone is watching.

While you're fumbling around for your phone, the disc silently shoot upward and now sits motionless, parked 1,000 feet above you.

Afraid to look away for fear of missing something, you search fo your phone by hand. By feel your hand finally grasps your phone. Takin your eyes off the disc for a split second, you make a quick glance at it to loca your camera icon. Before you can raise it to your eye, the disc darts off incredible speed.

It vanishes in the blink of an eye. The entire event is over in less than 60 seconds. You're left standing by your car, stunned by what you've just experienced.

There's nothing wrong with your vision. You're sober and not a drug user. Remembering your high school physics, you know that the human body can't survive the g-forces in a vehicle accelerating to such speed.

You decide it's your duty to file a report with someone. To invoke a cliché, "Who you gonna call?" Surely, someone in government is responsible for investigating such things. Where do you start?

There's no real urgency, so you find a non-emergency telephone number for your local police and call. You're routed to a desk sergeant. You explain, "This isn't a true emergency, but I saw something very strange that I'd like to report, can you help? I saw a silver disc…."

As you're telling him about the disc you just witnessed and giving him the location, he interrupts you. "Madam," he asks, "has a crime been committed?"

"No. Not that I'm aware of … but."

He cuts you off for a second time, "I'm very sorry. We investigate crimes. If a crime hasn't been committed, I suggest you call the Air Force."

Still determined, you call the nearest United States Air Force base. After listening to a lengthy menu, you finally speak with the base operator.

"Hello, I'd like to file a UFO report please. May I speak to whoever handles UFO sightings?"

"One moment. I'll transfer you to an information officer." You're placed on hold while an instrumental rendition of "Off We Go into The Wild Blue Yonder" plays in the background.

The music ends and as a recruitment commercial begins a man picks up. Without introduction and before you can get out a single word, he tells you politely, "I'm sorry, we don't investigate UFO sightings."

Frustrated, you tell him, "I'm not asking for an investigation. I'd like to file a report; can you at least take a report for me?"

"No, I'm sorry, we don't take reports either. I suggest that you call your local law enforcement agency." Click. You realize you've just made a complete circle and you're now back where you began.

No one is interested in UFO reports or photographic images other than the MUFON people. MUFON stands for the Mutual UFO Network. It's a civilian run organization that collects and investigates UFO sightings across the United States and Canada. No one in government will accept this data so it's simply warehoused. Sometimes it's shared with civilian UFO investigators.

Our government's official policy is one of disinterest when it comes to civilian sightings of UFOs. Then why does it devote taxpayer dollars to fund the world's biggest search for intelligent extraterrestrial life. It sounds contradictory.

Chances are that you've heard of SETI. In case you're unfamiliar, SETI is the "Search for Extraterrestrial Intelligence." SETI has been listening for intelligent signals from space since the 1970s. Since 1993, the project has been funded by The United States Government through NASA. If you're curious, look at NASA's budget at the Office of Budget Management (OBM)

SETI uses several huge radio telescopes that scan the sky by nigh and by day listening for intelligent radio transmissions from anywhere in th cosmos. Their capabilities have greatly expanded since the project was firs conceived in the 1970s. The growth of computer technology over the past 4 years allows SETI to search vast swathes of space that were previousl unexplored.

SETI is not really a search for extraterrestrial intelligence. SETI is search for radio signals, period. SETI is looking for analogue evidence in digital age.

Our government's interest in SETI is to find proof that alien li exists. But not here. The goal is to shift public attention from what's over ou heads to millions of miles away in deep space. The government might adm to proof of alien existence but only at arm's length. It is proof of the existence close to home that causes them discomfort. I'm reminded of a lir from a movie where a police officer tries to disperse a crowd by saying, "Just move along folks, nothing to see here."

Joseph Goebbels said, "Given the proper psychology it would not be impossible to prove to the masses that a square is in fact a circle." History has proven him correct many times. The drumbeat to the masses in 2018? "NASA's got everything under control. We're searching diligently for extraterrestrial life by scanning the skies for intelligent radio signals. Our land and orbital telescopes are discovering distant planets, new ones every day! Meticulously we are scanning the sky for radio waves. We're so close now!"

There are thousands of trustworthy people from all walks of life with reliable stories and incredible video evidence. Those sightings and witness reports, including film footage and photographs, are valuable. In the legal profession we call it evidence. The government directs our attention to outer space while the proof is in our own back yard. Sometimes literally.

At a Toronto conference in 2005, Paul Hellyer, a former Canadian Minister of Defence ("Defense" for US readers) announced publicly that UFOs and aliens exist. Unbelievably the world took little notice of his declaration. This was disclosure from a reliable person inside the highest echelon of government. Hellyer revealed that alien entities are here on Earth and some even live among us. He claimed that aliens from distant stars visit Earth regularly. Not one species of alien beings but perhaps a dozen! According to Hellyer, alien beings have been visiting Earth for thousands of years. Outrageous claims by any standard. But given the credibility of the ource, it's hard to dismiss.

In an article in the *Ottawa Citizen*, Hellyer "Demanded that world governments disclose what they know about their involvement with aliens." He said aliens possess the technology to reverse climate change and offer undreds of other things that could benefit mankind. But world governments keep this information secret. These discoveries our government has locked way. I wonder what marvelous secrets are locked away that could better the ves of everyone?

According to Hellyer, some world governments are in regular contact with ETs. He even claimed the United States Air Force works with aliens, de by side in the development of all manner of secret technology.

The world seems ready for full disclosure. If our government announced that intelligent alien beings are here and living among us it would be big news. But there'd be no rioting. There would be no frenzied crowds roaming the streets of New York and Hong Kong. No looting or global chaos would follow.

People are ready if not eager to hear the news. They've been ready for a hundred years. Intuitively, many people recognize that there are just too many sightings to deny their existence. Because sightings are now funneled to law enforcement agencies, I thought it wise to seek an opinion from a seasoned law enforcement officer. As a former district attorney, I have a few contacts in the legal community. I wanted to hear their perspective on UFOs. A Vermont police chief I've known for over a decade agreed to speak with me about his experiences. He was uncomfortable with the subject but agreed to a frank discussion so long as I respected his anonymity and didn't disclose his jurisdiction.

The chief admitted he has a file cabinet in his office devoted solely tc UFO reports. He said, "It's damn near full. I hope there's enough room in the bottom drawer to see me to retirement." I asked him how long his agency hac been compiling UFO reports. His answer surprised me. "My personal report only go back about six years. I inherited the bulk of the files from my predecessor and from chiefs before them going back to the mid-1930s."

When I asked if he believes ETs visit Earth, he didn't hesitate "There's not a doubt in my mind. Now I personally have never seen a thing But I have two deputies who claim they saw three cylinder-shaped objects fl across [location redacted]. My deputies were in different locations and i different vehicles. They reported their sightings to dispatch within minutes c each other. If they tell me they saw it, I believe them, … they were prett shaken up about it too."

In 1899, Nicola Tesla, a brilliant and under-recognized genius of th early 20th century, claimed to have received a radio transmission from Mar But Tesla lacked the credibility to back up his observation and conclusion. H needed evidence to support his claim. Without proof it was too extraordina a statement to be believed. Tesla's claim underscores Carl Sagan's quot "Extraordinary claims require extraordinary evidence."

Intelligent alien civilizations may intentionally choose to have an ılisted number. Announcing their presence by broadcasting into the vastness space could have unwanted consequences. They might have well-reasoned otives to keep quiet and maintain a low profile. Perhaps they've learned a rd lesson we have yet to learn.

No one else in the universe may be broadcasting. But we sure are. e've been unwittingly announcing our presence to the universe for seventy-ve years. *The Twilight Zone* has been traveling across the cosmos at the eed of light since the 1950s.

More concerning to many is that SETI is not just devoted to listening. TI has been actively broadcasting messages into space since 1974. SETI's gnals are much more powerful than a 1950's television broadcast. In 2008, TI and its partners beamed a powerful signal into deep space. It was inted toward a region believed most likely to be inhabitable. What was their essage? It was a Beatle tune from 1970 by John Lennon, "Across the iiverse."

We are shouting into the darkness.

In 2015, Stephen Hawking cautioned the world against broadcasting gh-energy radio signals into space. Our broadcasts are targeted toward laxies we believe could support intelligent life. Hawking warned, "When advanced civilization meets a less advanced civilization our world had oven it will not go well for the less advanced civilization." I'm sure his ords strike a chord of empathy with Native Americans.

Bill Gates and Elon Musk joined with Hawking to warn against vertising our existence. Collectively they concluded we could be inviting ings that are not benign space brothers.

The wording is clumsy, but the message is clear. In 2006 an article blished in the respected scientific journal *Nature* warned that the risk posed SETI broadcasts is real. The article cautioned that world contact with traterrestrial entities, even benign ones, could have "serious repercussions." early a decade before Stephen Hawking's warning other academics reached e same conclusion and raised the alarm.

If contacted, they may not offer us technology and scienti advancement for free. There may be a quid pro quo. But the terms may not to our liking. They may not barter at all. They might just take whatever th like. Our signals could be intercepted by intergalactic opportunis Malevolent beings well organized and seeking new worlds to pillage cou well be listening. Their agenda could be to enslave the unfortunate inhabitar of less sophisticated worlds or maybe worse. It rings of science fiction but i worth contemplation.

We take for granted human qualities like mercy, empathy, love, a ethics. We assume compassion will advance at the same rate as technolog Unfortunately, mankind's history doesn't support that assertion. T genocidal atrocities of the twentieth century are a compelling testament mankind's failure to advance. In a world of plenty, millions struggle survive without adequate nutrition, medical care and education.

Alien entities might view our world as so unsophisticated that hum life is insignificant to them. They may treat us the way we treat microb under a microscope slide. They might destroy civilizations the same way discard a petri dish loaded with living spores. It's a sobering thought.

The oldest documented UFO sighting I can find is from almost 3,5 years ago. It occurred in the year 1440 BCE. "Fiery discs in the sky" we seen over Southern Egypt and were recorded by Thutmose III's scrib Contemporaneously and independently, the same sightings were al recorded in the Tulli papyrus.

This was a UFO sighting made by two independent witness unknown to each other and separated by distance. Sightings with two or mc independent witnesses are more believable. Probably the best example w the Phoenix, Arizona mass sighting in 1997.

On March 13, 1997, thousands of residents of Phoenix reported a ve large, boomerang-shaped formation of lights over the Sierra Estre Mountain Range. It's a curious coincidence that a bright comet named Ha Bopp was crossing over Phoenix that same evening. This accounts for t staggering number of Arizonians that were watching the sky that nig Everyone was hoping for a glimpse of the comet. What most saw w something completely different.

Witnesses reported a "string of light" miles across and moving in perfect unison more like an enormous single object. They claimed that between the lights the stars were blotted out of the night sky as the object past overhead. All the witnesses swore that what they witnessed was a single enormous object instead of a string of lights.

The United States Air Force claimed the lights were flares dropped by aircraft during a routine exercise. That explanation was debunked. The Air Force takes all atmospheric conditions into consideration before planning an exercise over a populated area. It's common practice to make a press release in advance so folks can expect to see something odd in the night sky. We are to believe the USAF scheduled an exercise that involved dropping brilliant flares on the same night and the same time that a comet was due to traverse the Phoenix sky? It's hard for me to believe.

I guess I'm an unapologetic conspiracy theorist. I believe the United States Government is a party to the process. They work collaboratively to advance an agenda that will become known to all of us who live long enough. As a lawyer, I've been trained to collect and present evidence. I intend to present my experiences to you truthfully and without embellishment. Take from it what you will and if nothing else, please enjoy the story of my misfortune.

We have already opened our doors to monsters. They have arrived.

Incident at Devil's Den

I grabbed the cooler from the trunk and inventoried what we had. Most of the ice had melted. Still the beer was a few degrees below tepid. I busted out a package of hot dogs and a bag of badly smashed buns. I opened a bag of chips and a bag of cookies.

I skewered eight hot dogs and promptly burned all eight over the blazing brushfire I called a campfire. While Toby finished off his details, I assembled two plates of food.

We sat down, and Toby stared at his plate with the four black hot dogs. He never said a word. A hot meal was good. It's true that things taste better when cooked over an open flame. Even burnt hotdogs. We inflated our air mattresses and lounged around by the campfire.

The scent of the wood fire was pleasant in the way my grandfather's pipe tobacco had a pleasant aroma. We were content with listening to the crackle of the fire and watching the flames dance. The woods behind us were alive with singing crickets and tree frogs.

I said, "Hey, Tobe! This must be the allure of camping!"

"Yeah man, see! We worked out the bugs, we know how to do this stuff now," Toby bragged.

I agreed, "Man, we paid our dues and now we're outdoorsmen." It was turning into a pleasant evening.

My eyes adjusted to the encroaching darkness. The campfire was dwindling but it still gave us enough light to enjoy the evening and relax. Getting to sleep would not be a problem tonight.

The sky that night was unbelievable. Without light pollution or clouds, the stars were ten times brighter than the night sky we were accustomed to seeing.

Toby pointed out various stars and constellations. The stars were time machines according to Toby. The light from the stars we see could have taken millions of years to reach us traveling at light speed. They showed us an image of what was when the light left that star.

I hadn't given that much thought before. We could never observe the universe in real time. Even light from our sun was eight minutes old when it reached us. Relaxing on our air mattresses in the dark, we turned our full attention to the night sky. This night I noticed the dusty glow of the Milky Way! I'd never seen it so clearly before. It really was like a cloud spread across the sky.

"Toby, this is pretty goddamn cool. I bet this is how our ancestors entertained themselves for thousands of years."

"That's right," he agreed. I think he was proud of his plan.

"Toby, just think, before there were televisions, people sat around a radio. Before that, the hearth was the evening gathering place for warmth and cooking. Before that, people sat by a campfire every night like we were doing at that moment."

"Yeah, Terry, it's kind of humbling," added Toby.

Over small talk, we polished off a final beer apiece. Our campfire had dwindled to the red radiance of embers. Darkness closed in like a fog, but it was okay. Our eyes had somewhat adjusted and the stars gave us enough light to see the meadow floor and the horizon. That's all we needed. "Serene" was the best word I could think of to describe the moment.

When our laughter faded everything fell still. It felt peaceful for a while. Then I noticed the forest was now silent. Not a single tree frog or cricket. Nothing. There were none of the other noises you expect to hear in the forest at night. Just an hour earlier the forest had been alive with noise. But now everything was so still it made me a little uneasy. It felt unnatural. I wanted Toby's opinion.

I said, "Toby, listen! … Now that the fire's almost gone, I can't hear the crickets anymore. I can't hear anything! Is that normal you think?"

He paused for a moment to listen. It was eerily silent. "They'll be back. Just wait an hour and they'll be back again." But Toby sounded a little less than confident.

We relaxed. Aside from a few missteps, we'd triumphed over a day spattered with disappointments. We did some cool exploring. We hiked probably six miles and enjoyed the beauty of the forest. No state campground would have given us the opportunities we had here. Any campground would have felt like a parking lot in comparison. Even the isolation was peaceful. Everything was calm. But the stillness of the forest had me unnerved.

I was still puzzled by our unscheduled nap in the woods. I chalked it up to a six-hour drive and the hike. There was no other explanation. I put it aside and just enjoyed the night sky.

I saw Toby turn his head away from me. Something odd caught his eye to the west. There were three identical points of light sitting low in the western sky. Toby asked, "Hey, check it out! Were those there a few minutes ago?"

"What? Those what?" I strained my eyes thinking maybe Toby's pulling my leg. "Toby, don't feed me that ..."

"Right there," said Toby. "I don't think those are stars!" Toby pointed to three brilliant stars in a perfect little triangle sitting above the western horizon.

It took a moment of searching before I saw what he was talking about. Then I caught them. Each star was equidistant from the others. They sat stationary in the night sky. Whatever they were, they were interesting. They looked like three very bright stars. All three were identical to one another and they twinkled in the night sky like very bright stars. For a while, we just watched.

Toby broke the silence, "At least they're not like that freaky globe thing! That was weird."

"Yeah it was freaking weird, Tobe!" We both feigned a laugh.

Toby said, "They look like bright stars to me. I don't know every goddamn star in the universe, but I know clusters and I notice when something looks peculiar. Terry, these are ... peculiar."

"I agree, those are not stars, Toby. There are no aircraft lights set-up in a configuration like that. So, what are they?" I asked.

Toby didn't answer my question. I had expected an explanation. We watched them for a quarter hour. They were now the focus of our attention.

We both kept our eyes glued to these three points of light, sitting stationary. They were now brighter than when we first began watching them.

Toby spoke up again. This time breaking twenty minutes of silence, "Man, they're not aircraft and they're just sitting there. They're awfully damn bright too. There's no airfield around here, is there?"

"Nope," I told Toby. "Other than marijuana smugglers, who'd land a plane in a forest? This meadow is the only flat piece of land around for miles. It might be wide enough for a small airplane to set down."

"There!" Toby spotted it before me.

They were moving! It was exciting! We both spoke over one another. I said, "What the hell?" Neither of us had an answer. But it was cool. It was damn cool. I'd go as far as awesome.

While we watched, the three stars began to move. They slowly rotated as if on an axis. Unbelievable! All the while they maintained their perfect triangular configuration. The three lights moved in perfect harmony as if they were connected. For that reason, we suspected it might be a single solid object.

"Toby, if they are moving independent of one another, someone has choreographed this beautifully," I said.

"You got that right!"

I asked, "Toby, you're the astronomer. What the hell moves…?"

I left my sentence unfinished. I knew Toby had no idea either. There really was nothing to say. But we were spellbound.

"Hey man, are you as sleepy as I am?" asked Toby.

"Hell yeah, Tobe. We've been lying here watching this thing for an hour," I said with a yawn, "I'm beat … this day kicked my ass."

It began a vertical ascent. We watched it slowly climb the horizon. The points of light brighter as they crawled upward. These were not aircraft lights of any kind. This was something else entirely. I'm unsure how long we lay there just watching this thing. It was gaining altitude and incrementally increasing in brilliance and in size.

Toby didn't bother to use his cheap camera. His little camera was good for birthday parties but not long distant shots. We needed a camera and a telephoto lens like the one sitting on my kitchen counter.

We were content to just lay there and watch. Hardly a word was spoken between us. In the years following, I will question our passive behavior that evening. It was too dark to see my watch, but I estimated it to be near 11:00 PM. The triangular formation grew larger and sped up a little.

Toby said, "Man … they're really moving now."

I don't recollect responding. My eyes were stuck to them and I had nothing to add. It was moving even faster and blocking out entire fields of stars as it climbed. It was impossible to estimate its speed since we had no point of reference. Likewise, altitude was impossible to gauge without knowing the object's size and location. Puzzled at how big or near this thing could be, I asked, "Toby, could we be seeing lights that are a million miles away or could they be cruising at aircraft altitude?"

"Terry, man, that thing is in our atmosphere. It can't be outside of this solar system. No way. This thing is close. Man, I hope it's at cruising height … 35,000 feet would make me happy. No, I think it looks bigger because it's getting closer to us. It's … really close."

Toby said it first and confirmed what we both were thinking, "That's a single solid object. No doubt about it! Watch it pass over a field of stars. They blink out for a second or two and then blink back on as it goes past."

"I noticed that… Toby." With a feigned laugh, I said, "I think that damn thing is headed toward us. I think it's going to sail right over the top of us."

Toby didn't say a word. Once more, I noticed how quiet the entire forest was. The crickets and tree frogs had not returned as Toby had predicted. It wasn't worth mentioning at the time. I felt uneasy but not frightened…yet. I asked, "Toby are we safe here?"

"Man, I sure hope so," Toby said. After a pause he added, "What could hurt us…?"

I wasn't quite sure if that was a question requiring a reply. I said nothing. We both watched as its path placed it directly over the meadow. Then it abruptly stopped.

"Toby, it's not moving anymore is it?"

"Nope ..."

It came to a halt directly over our heads. While we watched the three points of the triangle spread further and further apart, eating up entire fields of stars as it grew. In a sky that was loaded with billions of stars, it was like someone cut a giant triangle out of the sky. This was a single object and it was enormous.

The three stars on each point of the triangle were so bright that the entire meadow glowed as brilliantly as the full moon. It was bright enough to cast shadows.

All the anxiety had left me. Once it had parked over the meadow, all emotion left me. We lay on air mattresses completely fascinated. We both just surrendered and let the calmness wash over us. It was pleasant, even soothing.

Grabbing our marginal flashlight, Toby said, "I'm going to try and signal it and see what happens."

Before I could object, Toby picked up the flashlight he held on his lap. Aiming it straight up, he flashed the light three times.

I said, "Man, that might get someone's attention!" We waited to see what would happen. We didn't have to wait long for something to happen.

In an instant, a beam of white light no wider than a softball was focused on our now dead campfire. It was about eight feet from where we lie. The light beam itself was visible. Like a high-powered search light shining through the fog. We never saw the beam descend. It was like someone threw a switch and there it was. It rested in the center of our fire pit.

Looking up, we traced the source of the light beam. It came from below and center of the triangle. It stayed for no more than thirty seconds and was gone. Poof! It just shut off.

A few minutes passed. Then a blue light struck the campsite. It was tiny compared to white light but much more intense. It was only the diameter of a pencil or narrower. Lasers were still a new concept in 1977. I'd seen them on television. Just like the white light that preceded it, this blue light originated from the center of the triangle.

This intense blue light beam actively darted about the campsite. We never saw it move. Instead it would blink out and a millisecond later it was back on a different spot. Striking haphazardly, it darted all over our campsite never sitting on anything for more than a few seconds. It darted back and forth, and it had a hypnotic quality to it as we watched. I'm certain it landed on my leg and chest at least once. I saw it land on Toby once or twice too. Then it abruptly stopped. It was with us for no longer than one or two minutes.

With the blue light gone, we lay there silent and ambivalent. I had no emotion other than a pleasant feeling of sedation. This huge thing was still nearly over the meadow and we just watched it without comment. Then Toby said something like, "Show's over," or words to that effect. I don't think I replied.

Those were the last words spoken between us that evening. In unison, we picked up our air mattresses and crawled into our tent. I felt the need to keep my boots on and laced up tightly. For that matter, I didn't bother to undress at all.

The apathy felt all too familiar. These things, whatever they are and whoever they are, controlled our actions and our emotions. This was the same apathy I experienced in 1966. Thoughts about that 1966 experience flashed in my mind briefly.

I was asleep the moment my head hit the inflated plastic pillow. The heat was tolerable now, almost pleasant, but the forest was still dead silent. The only sound was Toby snoring softly.

Surviving

"Being abducted by alien beings

is akin to getting your arm caught in a piece of farming equipment,

you may get loose, but you'll surely lose something in the process."

Terry Lovelace

It was the lights that woke me up. I first noticed the bright lights and then that low bass hum I'd heard before, except this was more intense. Some flashes of light were bright enough to illuminate the tent's interior as if we'd had an overhead light.

My eyes were sensitive to the lights. When I maneuvered my body to get to my knees, I realized I was in a lot of pain. Every bone in my body ached. I was insanely thirsty and scared too. I couldn't grasp what was happening to us and it was hard to shake off the sleep. I finally achieved a crouching position and my focus turned to Toby.

Toby was on his knees inside the tent. He had opened the tent flap about two inches and was peering out at something in the meadow. He was crouched down and captivated by whatever was happening there. Again, he muttered something, but I couldn't make out what he was saying

The lights outside were multicolored greens and yellow. Very bright and in quick doses like a camera flash or a strobe light. I was awake but still in a fog.

I wondered if this could be park rangers with flashlights? Or maybe the headlights of a park service jeep with emergency lights flashing? But these were multicolored lights. That just didn't fit. I was struggling to fully wake up. I had to claw my way to consciousness.

It wasn't only the lights. There was also that droning sound. At first, I thought it was noise made by a generator. Who would be running a generator in the bed of a pickup truck? Game poachers maybe? The flashes of light illuminated the inside of the tent just enough to catch an image now and then.

I saw Toby was trembling like a man in the cold. I realized I was trembling too.

I reached for the flashlight and Toby roughly snatched it from my hand. He held his finger across his lips and whispered, "Be quiet, they're still out there!"

I was shocked! In the flashes of light, I could see tracks down Toby's cheeks. He'd been crying! This is a man I knew well. We were first responders and we'd been through some dangerous moments together as a team. Toby could be relied upon to keep his head and not panic in an emergency. This felt like an emergency. What could move Toby to tears?

Toby continued to shush me when I tried to speak. With my voice just above a whisper I asked, "Toby, what is it? Tell me what's wrong? Are there park rangers outside?"

Toby shook his head "no" and stayed fixated on whatever was happening outside our tent. I noticed his breathing was shallow and quick, nearly panting.

I kept my voice at a whisper, "Toby, man, you got to slow your breathing down. You're hyperventilating. Toby you've got to tell me what's going on damn it."

Then I froze. I was startled by motion outside the tent. There were shadows crossing between the tent and the source of the lights. I heard footsteps too. There was a rustling of leaves and grass. I had the impression maybe a dozen people were walking around the campsite. We both froze until the noises stopped.

The apathy we'd experienced before bed was long gone. In its place was abject terror and panic. I tried once more to get through to my friend.

"Toby, tell me what happened? Tell me who's out there?" I asked. But why even ask? I knew who was out here. I knew them.

Toby didn't answer me. I thought he was in shock. Frustrated, I struggled to knees to see what was going on in the meadow. With my left arm I pushed Toby back a bit and gathered the courage to look for myself. I was fully awake now and the mental fog had mostly lifted.

Squeezing next to Toby, I pulled back the canvas and there it was. This wasn't a flying saucer at all! It was something else, something much bigger. This was something I had never seen before and was unprepared for. It was so gigantic that it filled every inch of the meadow. It sat motionless in mid-air. I estimated it to be thirty feet off the meadow floor.

Then it registered. Of course, this is the thing we watched last night! Before we went to sleep in the tent, we had been staring at something in the sky! I remembered we were watching the triangle in the sky, but it was about 2,500 feet above us last evening. This was the thing that generated so much disinterest in us just hours earlier? Unbelievable.

Now it was thirty feet over the meadow. We could see two sides clearly. There were randomly disbursed square panels of light on each side. It reminded me of a five-story office building at night with offices lit here and there on every floor. Along the very top was a row of larger windows that slanted outward. They were all lit. I saw faint shadows and movement behind these larger panels. These larger panels stretched the entire length of the two sides of the triangle we could see.

The points of light had dimmed and were flashing. They were changing colors from greens, yellows, and orange. Along with the droning sound, these were the colored lights that woke me. The forest was quiet but for a low droning sound that reverberated in my chest.

Toby shoved his way over my left shoulder now and we watched together. We saw figures walking and milling around underneath this thing. My God they were children! Maybe a dozen or more kids, all about the same height. They were milling about in small groups of two or three.

I whispered to Toby, "What the hell are children doing here underneath this giant thing in the middle of the night?"

There was fear in Toby's voice when he answered, "Those ain't little kids. Those are not human beings Terry. They took you too … they hurt us both. Terry, they hurt us…" His voice faded into soft sobbing again. I placed my left arm across his shoulder, and he leaned against me, crying like a child.

Images flashed in my mind and I recalled dreadful things. "Toby, I know." I shut them out.

I shifted my focus back to the craft as Toby struggled to compose himself. The thing was mind-blowing. I tried to take in the details. Its size alone made it a threat. It was made of black metallic material that was non-reflective. I would call the finish matte, like the diamond thing we saw. The corner nearest to us was the source of the multi colored lights we saw shining through the canvas of our tent. The lights on each point shined through a seamless panel that ran from the bottom to the very top. It was the three corner lights that we initially mistook for stars in the sky. They shined brilliant white lights that twinkled to give the casual observer the impression they were just three stars in a field of billions.

Turning my head, I glanced through the little screen window in the rear of the tent. Behind us the entire forest was dimly lit with long shadows. That sight unnerved me too. I knew I did not want to leave the tent.

A column of white light was now pouring out of something that was in the dead center of the craft's bottom. I estimated the diameter of this shaft of light to be thirty feet and perfectly round. It was a visible cylinder of light.

I was scared to death! But I didn't want to take my eyes off it. We saw the little people walk into the broad beam of light and dissolve into it. They continued moving under the light and disappearing two or three at a time. They were leaving. We watched until the last one was gone.

Shortly after the last little person vanished the center light switched off. The corner lights went to all white and were as bright as sunshine. The hum was gone now. The meadow was silent again.

We were on our bellies with just our heads sticking out of the tent. We watched. We both felt like something was about to happen. Something did.

The whole thing began to rise like a hot-air balloon. It slowly rotated clockwise a half turn and wobbled slightly. It continued to climb, and it picked up speed until it was back in the heavens again. We watched the three points of light grow dimmer and closer together. Eventually it was just three dim dots of light forming a small triangle. This was the reverse of what we witnessed earlier in the evening. It didn't shoot out of sight or slide down to the horizon. It just continued its steady ascent until it vanished.

Toby spoke up, “It’s gone now.” He had regained control of his breathing and returned to his senses. I felt a little better too. But I ached all over and I was still terrified.

I had some memories of what had just happened to us inside the craft. I could see scant color images. I could recall a whirring noise and a sense of motion. Then a flash of bright light and we were suddenly inside the spacecraft. We were sucked into the thing just like the little people we watched dissolve into the light. I remember being awestruck by the volume of its interior. Everything was either in white or stainless steel. The structure was brilliantly lit inside. The ceiling and wall panels emitted light.

I was astounded to see three flying saucers parked inside. They were aligned in a neat row at the far side. We could see walkways and different levels. I recalled inside there were support structures and unrecognizable symbols etched into the walls.

We were not alone. Inside we saw fifty or sixty other people. Afterward, I wondered who they were and what happened to them? Did they leave with the machine? Were they even still alive? I knew that I was fortunate to be alive.

There’s a psychiatric disorder known as “survivor guilt.” It happens when you survive a life-threatening event that others did not. Toby and I made it back, but I’m not sure those poor souls ever made it home. I sure as hell wouldn’t change places with them.

I knew there had to be more. A lot more. But those few memories were the extent of my recall.

Many years later, events would happen to bring those memories back and into sharp focus. I recalled sights and voices I was supposed to forget. Like Betty and Barney Hill, it would need to be dredged up from my subconscious. They could suppress the memories but never erase them.

The spacecraft was gone, and we sat upright afraid to speak above a whisper. Then I noticed my boots. My boots had been tightly laced before I lay down. I kept them that way intentionally. Now, they were unlaced more than half-way down. That made no sense. I pulled them both off and discovered my socks were on crooked as well. I put them back on properly. Glancing to my left, I noticed Toby was lacing-up his boots too.

I was aware of the pain again. Every fiber in my body ached. I felt sick and nauseous. But most of all, I was thirsty. I was insanely thirsty.

Toby rummaged around the tent and found the last warm can of beer. I had a gallon jug half-full of warm water. We split them both and craved more. Never in my life had I been so thirsty. It crossed my mind that I could take it all. I could gulp it down before he could stop me. I squelched that idea. I forced myself not to dwell on the thirst for fear I'd lose my mind.

"Toby, no matter what the hell just happened to us, we need to pull it together. I want to get to the car and get the hell off this goddamn meadow."

Toby nodded in agreement.

We needed a plan of action. Just like camping, this wasn't rocket science.

Toby had a plan, "I got this flashlight to read my map. I say we bolt out of this tent and into the car. You drive, and I'll tell you where to go. The maps still in the glove box. It's the same thing we did to find this place but in reverse. Man, we can do this."

Toby's confidence bolstered my own.

"Okay, you're right, Tobe. Let's make a run for the car. You carry the flashlight and I've got my wallet and keys," I said with determination.

We readied ourselves. It sounds odd but leaving the tent and being in the open and exposed was a chilling thought. In the short distance we'd sprint to the car, we'd be exposed and vulnerable. I hoped we'd feel safer once inside the car. The Impala offered locking doors and high-beam headlights. Most importantly, it gave us mobility. I grabbed the rusty kitchen knife too. For what purpose, I don't know. I just felt better with the knife in my hand.

Toby nodded with approval. I was sure he could use his map to guide us back. So long as his batteries held out. If we lost our flashlight, our ability to navigate would be severely compromised.

I unzipped the tent all the way and we bolted for the car without a word said.

Toby was out first, and I followed. With nothing but starlight to see, we sprinted the 20 yards to the car. I stumbled at least once. Toby reached the car before me, but he was locked out. I locked the car purely out of habit.

I made it to the car a second or two behind Toby. I unlocked the driver's door and dove in. I slid across the plastic bench seat and unlocked Toby's door as I slammed my door shut behind me. With Toby inside, we both locked our respective sides of the car. It started right up. I kicked on the high beams and we were ready. The dome light stayed on for about sixty seconds. It was long enough to check the back seat and floorboard.

Before pulling out, Toby asked urgently, "Are we good? Are you sure we're good?"

I understood him clearly, "We're good to go," I said reassuringly.

Toby's focus was dedicated to his map and the road ahead. The flashlight grew dimmer by the minute. Every now and then he'd reach over and turn on the dome light for a few seconds to better study his map. He needed the light to read the map but the light inside the car made me blind. I couldn't see the road. Not that there was anything outside that I wanted to see save the road in front of me. What caused two grown men to flee like scared little boys? Whatever happened on the meadow triggered a deep fear in the both of us. I was acquainted with the feelings. The disinterest and apathy were nothing new.

There was a reason my boots were unlaced. It was inadvertent validation by my captors. It was as much evidence as a curtain tucked into the venetian blinds. It was as good as a toy airplane on the floor. There's no way Toby and I just experienced the same dream or same hallucination. This was a real experience. Thirst was an immediate problem. But a solution would have to wait until we had some distance between us and that damn meadow.

This must be the kind of fear that men are born with. It comes from down deep in the lower part of our brainstem. This can't come from the cognitive part of the brain we use in decision-making. This came from a much older part of the brain. A leftover from our early evolutionary development.

The same applied to our fear of the dark. Maybe that was a leftover from the long nights our distant ancestors endured? In the darkness of night, the tables were turned for them. Man became the prey. An unseen adversary had already gotten the drop on us while we were sleeping. Now was the time for flight because we were now the prey.

The car was made without seatbelts. It was all I could do to keep a grip on the steering wheel. Toby was violently tossed around inside the car like some crazed carnival ride. The high beams danced ahead of me as the car bounced along the road. Sometimes they lit up the road. On hills, they shown up in the trees and sometimes just two feet in front of us on the down side. Other than the two piercing headlights, we were enveloped by darkness.

I thought briefly about what we had left behind. We abandoned a perfectly good tent and air mattresses back there. The backpack with Toby's camera and our blankets were still inside the tent. We could care less. Our focus was drink, distance, and home—in that order.

We passed the two posts where the road had been chained. Then I knew we were alright. I could find my way through the park and back to the road by myself. I complimented Toby for getting us back inside the park safely. But Toby lay sideways on the seat in a semi-fetal position. He was already snoring.

I shifted my focus to staying alert and staying on the road. The sunshine was so intense it was excruciating. My eyeballs ached.

It was mid-morning before Toby stirred. He broke the quiet hum of the road, "Man, get us something to drink, please." His voice was raspy like mine.

"Toby, I'm as thirsty as you are," I said. "I'll pull over at the next gas station we find. Hang on, Tobe," I said, trying to sound reassuring.

"That sounds good. I'm just so damn thirsty."

I asked Toby, "Hey, look around the car again. See if you can find us something else to drink. I'll drink anything wet that won't poison me."

Toby rummaged through the car for a jug or bottle. He searched for anything we could drink, "Sorry man, there's nothing left."

Still groggy from his sleep Toby was struck by the intensity of the sun and his thirst. Like me he was in pain from unbearable body aches. I felt flushed. I must have been feverish. Fever was the cause of the body aches and the thirst, I reasoned. I itched all over too. It was that creepy feeling like I've heard people say they felt "bugs crawling under their skin." That's how it felt.

I couldn't recall a time ever in my life when I felt so parched. The sunlight was so intense. I wore a cheap pair of sunglasses, but they were worthless. My eyes stung as if I'd stared at the sun.

I said, "Toby, man this sunshine is killing me!"

Toby just nodded. His eyes were nearly swollen shut.

Soon we pulled into a "Gas 'n Go" touting, "the coldest beer in town." It was pretty much a clone of the place we hit on the way down. Just another generic stop for farmers and travelers. I'm sure it was indispensable for the locals. The second we stopped rolling, I jumped out of the car and ran to the restroom. I shouted over my shoulder to Toby, "I'll be quick."

I noticed my legs were unsteady. Knocking on the beat-up steel door I yelled out with urgency, "Hello!" After a minute or two with no reply I made my way inside to find the key for the men's room.

An elderly gentleman manned the cash register. He appeared to be in his eighties but looked spry and sturdily built. He wore a tee shirt and well-worn overalls. He was waiting for me with a broad smile, a restroom key in hand.

I snatched it from his hand, "Thank you!" The restroom key was fastened by a length of chain to a foot-long piece of 4x4. Whoa! They must have a serious problem with people driving away with their restroom key. I made it back to the men's room probably moments before I would have pissed myself.

Predictably, the place was filthy. There was no window and the only light came from a single buzzing neon tube. Stepping up to the urinal, I relieved myself for what felt like five full minutes. I thought to myself, "God, no wonder I'm dehydrated." I went to the sink and was shocked when I saw my reflection in the mirror. It took a moment to register. My face was puffy and red, and my eyes were nearly swollen shut. Pulling my tee shirt over my head I saw dozens of angry red sores evenly dispersed and covering my entire face and torso. I dropped my pants to find that red spots covered both of my legs down to my boots. They itched savagely.

We had regularly doused ourselves down with military grade DEET. I expected to suffer a mosquito bite or two, but this was insane. I looked like a smallpox victim.

Then I saw how badly sunburned I was on my face and arms. My whole body was beet red. My upper arms, even under my arms were badly burned. Thankfully, I wasn't blistered. I used DEET and sunscreen so what the hell? Did they cancel out one another when combined? I was searching for an answer but that was nonsense.

I had no tan lines whatsoever. To be burned so evenly I would have to had been fully nude in direct sunlight and rotated like a chicken on a rotisserie. How else could my body be so evenly burned?

Splashing tepid water all over my head and chest, I rinsed myself off as best I could. The water felt good. It felt like ice water when I splashed it on my chest. I didn't bother to dry off. I soaked my tee shirt so the wind from the highway could help cool me down on the last leg of our trip. I still felt feverish. The thirst was still with me. Cupping my dirty hands under the grungy faucet to drink, I noted my hands were shaking. I drank and drank from what trickled out of the dirty faucet. Repeating the process, I drank until I felt I could hold no more.

I opened the metal door. Standing there was a pathetic looking Toby, patiently waiting. He looked like he could fall over any instant. He was unsteady. He leaned against the cinderblock wall to keep from toppling over.

Crap, if I looked bad, Toby was a train wreck by comparison. In addition to the insect bites, Toby's eyes were red like mine. His entire face was swollen sufficiently to distort his features. He complained of the burn on his black skin. He was in agony.

I handed Toby the restroom key. I said, "No worries, pal. I'll finish the drive and you can go back to sleep."

"Thanks, Terry," Toby said as he pushed his way past me and into the men's room.

The second I stepped outside, I was momentarily blinded by the sun. I pulled my sunglasses down and headed back inside to buy something cold to drink.

A bell over the door tinkled when I walked back inside the little store. The old man hadn't moved. I paid for our gas and bought a six-pack of orange soda.

"My buddy will be right back with the key," I said.

"That's okay, son. Nobody makes it too far away with the key," he said. I think the key thing must have been an inside joke. I sat my orange six-pack on the counter and held out a ten. He must have noticed my hands were shaking. He put on his glasses and eyed me up and down while he made change.

He was straight out of a farm equipment calendar. He wore the green tractor hat and well-worn overalls. A pouch of chewing tobacco sat next to the register. Alongside was an old diner-style coffee mug he used as a spittoon. The old guy looked me over a second time. Then he asked me with genuine concern, "It ain't none of my business, but what the hell have you fellers been into?"

I answered honestly, "I don't know." I shrugged my shoulders and returned his smile.

"You better get to someplace where you can get yourself some help," he said, before stuffing a golf ball-size chunk of chewing tobacco in his cheek. "You boys want to call somebody for a ride or something? You can use my phone if you want. Hell, I don't care," he said. He was the first bright spot in an otherwise miserable day.

"We're just headed to the air base. I think we'll be okay," I was touched by his concern for our safety. I thought, some people are born with empathy for others and some are born with none. I don't remember thanking him but I'm sure I did.

I heard the bell tinkle again as Toby stumbled inside to buy something to drink. He chose a gallon of grape drink for himself. I thought, he sure as hell isn't drinking any of this! Then I felt ashamed for my selfishness. I grabbed my orange soda and stumbled to the car. The sun was merciless. It hit me like a punch in the face.

I jumped into the driver's seat and re-adjusted my mirror. Simultaneously, Toby climbed into the passenger seat. He cuddled up with the gallon jug of grape-aid against his chest. I'm sure the cold jug felt good against his burned torso. Toby immediately began pounding the grape drink while I polished off six cans of orange soda, one after another. I craved more.

"Go back to sleep, Tobe. I got it the rest of the way." I knew there was no way he could drive a car.

We never once discussed the events of the past 12 hours. For that matter, we rarely spoke at all during the ride back. Something had changed. Things were different between us. We were different.

Toby mumbled, "God I can't wait to get back ..." and his voice trailed off.

Neither of us were in any mood for chitchat. He went back to his grape drink. In fifteen minutes, he had downed the last of it and returned to his fetal position. A few minutes later he was out like a light and snoring again. I envied him. I couldn't wait for my turn to shut my eyes.

Back on the road, a pounding headache behind my eyes made driving tougher than before. It was from the sunlight. The fever and body aches hadn't eased.

Soon, I fell back into the rhythm of the road and traveled on autopilot. The warm air from the highway completely dried my shirt before I made fifty miles. I was dangerously tired from lack of sleep and had no business driving. Toby was in worse shape than me. I couldn't give him the keys.

Have you ever been so tired that you begin dreaming while awake? Once I caught myself nod off for what seemed like a split second! I raised my head and when I opened my eyes I was in the lane of opposing traffic on my left. By the grace of God, the road was empty that morning. Had things been different, I could have killed us and probably another innocent soul or two. From that point on I concentrated on the road and staying awake. I had a newfound respect for long-haul truckers.

I reviewed the events of the previous night over and over. What happened to us once we were inside that giant airplane hangar? Something very bad had happened. Someone had hurt the both of us. Bits and pieces of terrible things floated by my mind's eye. I winced at the images and once or twice involuntarily yelled out, "No!" hoping to drive the scenes from my mind. I did my best to focus on something else.

My memories were like flipping through a stack of photographs under a strobe light. There were horrible images. There were garbled auditory sounds and voices with unintelligible words mixed together. I very clearly remembered Toby kept screaming!

Visually, it was limited to a series of disjointed images. I had no memory whatsoever of what may have occurred during our four-hour unscheduled nap on that outcropping of limestone. But I believe something happened.

From the time I entered the tent until that moment, I simply couldn't place events on a linear timeline. But in a flash of intuition, I surprisingly knew what had happened to us! We'd been set up! We were there by design. We had an appointment on the meadow that evening, and we arrived right on time. Looking back at this ridiculous camping trip idea and the way we went about it was almost comical. In a tragic way.

I couldn't speak the words out loud, but I knew they took me. I knew they took both of us. This wasn't anything like seeing a flying saucer. I'd seen flying saucers before, and it was a cool experience. It was exciting. I knew it was real because I validated that second event with a piece of curtain stuck into the venetian blinds. That happened when I was eleven years old. There was nothing cool about this experience and I had more than enough evidence to validate it. It would turn out that I had more evidence than I ever could have suspected.

I wondered if they took Toby when he was little. Maybe that's why he has such a fascination with space? It's a pity I would never have an opportunity to ask him. I glanced over to the softly snoring Toby. I could sense something was different between us and I didn't understand it. During the entire trip home there was only essential conversation. In retrospect, I'm not even sure Toby was asleep. He may have just faked it to avoid conversation. That was fine with me. I wasn't in my right mind.

It was a state of mind that I'd come to know even better in the days and years to come. It was sad that we returned so empty handed. There would be no laughing or making jokes over a beer at his barbeque. I wouldn't be teasing Toby about the starry-eyed farm girl. Forget everything. It was just not a topic for discussion. Ever.

We had promised to call our wives. This was the time before cell phones. But they didn't expect to hear from us for another day, so it was no big deal. I just sped toward home miserable and fighting to keep my eyes open and my car in the correct traffic lane.

If I had called home from the gas station using the old man's phone, what would I say? The old guy sat two feet away from the phone. That would have been a call he'd remember. I could just imagine the look on his face when he overheard that conversation. "Hi Hon! Yeah, we're headed back early. Why? Oh, well we saw a giant triangle that blotted out the stars and went to bed. Then there were crazy lights and we were dragged aboard a giant space ship. So, we're coming home early, and goddamn am I thirsty!"

I could just imagine the old guy swallowing his chaw of tobacco.

My mother's words came back to me, "Terry thinks he saw a spaceship and he's throwing a fit." I wanted to throw a fit. After an insanely miserable ride, we were finally close to home. It was time to wake up Toby. He'd been soundly asleep since downing his last drop of his grape-aid.

I announced, "Hey pal, our ETA is about fifteen minutes."

Toby mumbled something and stretched. I took it to mean, "okay" or some similar word of acknowledgement. He was having trouble adjusting his eyes to the sunlight. I was certain Toby was hurting more than I was.

Finally, we were back on base. First stop was Toby's house. I unceremoniously dropped him off in his driveway. Other than his flashlight he had no baggage to carry in. His backpack was back at the campsite. Our parting words were, "See ya."

We lived just a few blocks from Toby's. My wife heard me pull into the driveway. She was happy to see me but puzzled why the trip had been cut short?

"Glad to have you back, but why'd you come home so soon, you know you forgot your…?" She noticed something wasn't right.

I moved past her and sat at our kitchen table. I recall asking, "What do we have to drink? I am so thirsty."

She looked at me for a long moment before she spoke. All she could say was, "What the hell?" She poured me a tumbler full of lemonade. I drank it all in two gulps. She poured more. "How did this happen to you, Terry? Is Toby in the same shape?" she asked.

I shrugged my shoulders and mumbled, "I think Toby's worse."

She found the thermometer and took my temperature. Five minutes later she said, "Jesus, you've got a temp of almost 104!" She gave me some aspirin and drew me a cool bath.

In ten minutes, she had me undressed and soaking in cool water. She added baking soda or something that helped with the itching and the sunburn pain. It felt so good to just soak and relax in the water. I lay there for about 30 minutes guzzling instant lemonade on ice. She took my temperature again and it had dropped to just over 102.

"Come on! I'll help you get dressed we're going to the clinic," she said.

Before I knew it, I was in the exam room.

One of the doctors walked in with a look of concern. For some reason I expected him to ask, "What the hell you two fellers been into?" Like the old guy at the gas station who was so kind.

"Hey Terry, what the hell happened to you guys? You're both pretty sick. Brenda will draw some blood and push it through the lab, stat. Your wife tells me you were out with Tobias on a camping trip and came home this morning sick as dogs. Is that correct so far?"

I nodded.

He immediately began examining me while my favorite nurse, Brenda, drew a dozen tubes of blood. "You guys felt fine the evening before. Then you woke up sick, sunburned, and bug bitten and running a temp of 104? Is that right?"

"Yes, that's right."

He wanted the entire story, "Okay, tell me what happened to you guys."

I told him most of the story, leaving out all that happened between 9:00 PM the preceding evening and 3:00 AM early that morning. Most of it was a blur anyway.

I knew I'd end up on the psych ward if I told him the true story. So, I gave him my sanitized version and focused on my physical symptoms and not my recollections.

As I spoke, more and more people trickled into the room. I could hear my wife's voice in the hallway. I heard someone say, "Tobias." So, I knew Toby must be here too.

There were now three doctors, and a second nurse joined Brenda. Doctors came and went. I guess they were trying to treat both of us at the same time. I'm sure they were as perplexed as we were. It seemed that way. I didn't know it at the time, but we were classified as acutely ill.

I endured the most thorough medical examination of my life. It was difficult to know what was going on. My eyes ached and were sensitive to the light, so I kept them closed for most of the exam.

A medical assistant brought in a camera and photographed every single inch of my body. Brenda counted every red spot. The grand total was 124. At one point I heard the growl of a Geiger counter and got a glimpse of the signature yellow box.

I knew about radiation. I was on an air base with enough plutonium to destroy all Western Europe. I heard the Geiger counter growl. That concerned me. Exposure to radiation in the woods was an unsettling thought. Exposure to radiation inside a spaceship was too much to fathom.

One of the doctors asked Sheila to go home and bag up everything I brought back from the trip. He asked her to go right now and bring it all right back.

He gave her a large white bag with the Bio Hazard symbol on it and a drawstring at the top. He wanted everything I was wearing when I came home, boots, socks, dirty clothes the whole lot. He also wanted anything I brought home with me, like rocks or anything of the like.

I sure as hell didn't bring home any souvenirs.

My commanding officer came in. It was common knowledge throughout the unit that Toby and I were going on this camping trip. I wasn't sure how he'd react. He came to check on my condition. Like everyone else, he wanted to know how we both managed to get so sick.

I said, "Sir, I have no idea. But I'll be up and about for my Tuesday night shift."

"We can cover it if we have to, just get well, alright Ansel Adams? We want to see your photographs as soon as you get a few prints developed. Just get some rest."

I didn't know it at the time, but he reported the details of our hospitalization to the security police. I assume it was protocol because of the bizarre nature of our injuries and positive reading on the Geiger counter.

I told our CO thanks. Then I thought, Oh, God no. I won't have a single photograph to show him or anyone else. That seemed like the last indignity of the day. I fought to keep from crying.

The examination finally wrapped up. As the doctors left, Brenda helped me off the table and into a wheelchair. She also got me more ice water, which was very much appreciated.

"Doctor Sanders admitted you with a diagnosis of dehydration. That IV is running full-tilt so you should feel better soon."

I was relieved to hear I wasn't suffering from radiation poisoning.

Brenda assured me, "When Sheila comes back, we'll make sure she knows where to find you."

"Thank you so much. Brenda, you're so kind."

Special Agents

My first forty-eight hours in the hospital are a blur. I don't know what they gave me for pain, but I slept almost around the clock. They kept the lights off in my room unless needed, because I was still photophobic.

It was the evening of my last night in the hospital. I'd describe my condition as marginally okay. Hopefully well enough to go home in the morning. The CO gave me a week off duty to regain my strength. I needed every minute of it.

A nurse opened my door and two men in business suits followed her in. She ignored them and walked over to my bed and said, "Dr. Sanders ordered something to help you rest tonight. You'll be going home in the morning." She held a syringe and said she was going to give me something for pain. I could use it. Every bone in my body still hurt. At least the itching had abated.

The older of the two gentlemen intercepted her. He said, "If that's going to sedate him, it'll have to wait. We're from OSI and need to ask Sergeant Lovelace a few questions. This won't take long; shut the door on your way out." She was out like a shot and I didn't get my pain medicine. The instant the door was closed the older guy flipped on the overhead lights. It felt like I had sand in my eyes.

The OSI is the investigative arm of the USAF's Security Police. They are to the air force what NCIS is to the navy. They carried themselves like Gestapo.

"Sir, can you turn off the lights? Please. They hurt my eyes."

"We need to see what we're doing, son. We can't talk to you in the dark. This won't take long, I just have a couple questions," he said.

They introduced themselves as special agents from the OSI. They were all business and scared the hell out of me with their affect and demeanor. They showed me their badges. Since they wore civilian clothes, I inspected their credentials just long enough to catch their rank. The older guy was a major and his companion was a captain.

Each man grabbed a chair and they sat on opposite sides of the bed close to my head. The older guy commandeered control of my tray table and moved everything off the top. He slid it over my lap while his partner raised the head of my bed to a sitting position.

I'm fuzzy about the captain's name but I can clearly remember the older guy. He introduced himself as, "Special Agent Gregory." Agent Gregory was in charge and did most of the talking.

The captain introduced himself as, "Special Agent something." He set up a small reel-to-reel tape recorder on my tray table. He crossed his legs and balanced a notepad on his knee. He said very little but paid keen attention.

Special Agent Gregory spoke first, "Sergeant Lovelace, I'll be the special agent in charge of your case."

"Yes sir," I said. But I thought to myself, "I have a case?" What the hell does that mean? Did we burn down the forest? I knew the reputation of the OSI for being tough guys. I dared ask, "Agent Gregory sir, am I in trouble?"

He replied, "Son, you're asking me if you're in trouble? Would we be here if you weren't in trouble?" His reply amused the captain. My stomach turned. I caught the sarcasm in his tone. I sized him up as someone not to mess with. He wore a flattop haircut and had the chiseled square jaw look. His pistol was visible inside his unbuttoned suit coat.

Special Agent Gregory explained, "Sergeant Lovelace, we need to talk to you right now while everything is fresh in your mind. Do you understand? I know you're sleepy, but you need to stay alert. It's important that you answer my questions honestly and thoroughly. Do you understand me, Sergeant?"

I nodded.

Agent Gregory rolled his eyes. I saw he was annoyed, but I didn't know why. He took a laminated playing card from his breast pocket and put on some reading glasses. They rested on the very tip of his nose, so he could see over the top.

He read my rights under the Uniform Code of Military Justice also known as the UCMJ. He recited them like he'd read them a thousand times. The tone and tenor of his voice betrayed his distaste for the task. He took off his glasses and carefully put them away when he'd finished.

Without eye contact he asked, "Do you understand what I've told you?"

Once more I nodded and once more, he looked annoyed. Now he raised his voice, "Son, don't answer me with a nod of your head or a shrug of your shoulders. The captain here can't put that down in his notes and the tape recorder can't pick it up. Do you get it now? Now speak up!"

"Yes sir, now I understand," I said apologetically.

Reaching into his briefcase, Agent Gregory pulled out a manila folder and a few papers. On my tray table he carefully laid out six forms. He instructed me, "Son, these are waiver and consent forms. You're waiving your rights and giving us your consent for certain things. You're promising to cooperate fully and honestly with our investigation. You have the right to an attorney if you'd like. You can hire your own lawyer, or the JAG will appoint someone to represent you. You said you understood your rights. Do you understand them, or shall I read them to you again?"

"Yes, sir and no sir." I said. I believe he was intentionally mixing his questions, so they required mixed "yes" and "no" responses. It made the process difficult to follow. Probably an interrogation technique taught at the Gestapo academy.

Agent Gregory picked up where he left off, "By signing these consent forms you give us permission to conduct a search of your home and your car. We have your permission to seize anything we find without first securing a search warrant. We look for things such as contraband or anything that could be evidence of a crime. You don't have anything to hide from us, do you…son?"

"No sir," I said. I felt like voicing an objection would make me sound evasive or uncooperative. I was afraid of this guy.

"Let's be clear. You understand what I've said, and you are fine with all of it?"

I spoke up this time, "Yes, sir."

"Good," said Gregory, obviously pleased with himself. He used his finger to show me where to sign, "I need your signature here and here, sign here and here and here, here and the last one. I also need your initials here on the left. Very good…very good. Well done, sergeant."

I signed everything. I never read a single word of it. My eyes were still nearly swollen shut. Reading them would have been impossible. His explanations were woefully inadequate for a young and naïve NCO.

Gregory swooped up the forms and returned them to his manila folder. Projecting his voice in the direction of the tape recorder, Agent Gregory said, "This is Special Agent Gregory, in the matter of Sergeant Terry J. Lovelace, 351st Strategic Missile Wing …"

While he spoke, I closed my eyes because of the pain. I guess he thought I was falling asleep. Gregory startled me by shouting, "Pay attention! Stay with me and don't forget to speak up when you answer my questions. Got it son?!"

"Yes, sir," I understood him alright. I dared to ask a question, "Sir, is there a way we could do this after I've had some more sleep?"

They paused for a moment and looked at each other. I think they were amused.

Scowling at me, Agent Gregory said, "Look sergeant, I've already explained why we need to talk now. Are you rescinding your agreement to cooperate now?"

I said, "No, sir, I just …"

"You just what son? I read your rights and explained them. You claimed to understand them. You signed consent forms and waivers. Nobody twisted your arm or threatened you. Do you want me to tear these papers up now? If you'd like we can stop right this minute and we'll see each other again at your court martial," replied Gregory.

"No, sir, I mean, yes, sir, I'll cooperate…sir." The words "court martial" evoked all kinds of scenarios. None of them were good.

"Excellent! While all of this is fresh in your memory we want to get to the truth. The doctors want us to help them find an explanation for what's happened to you and your friend," he said.

"Yes, sir. I was just asking. I want to cooperate. I'll answer your questions, sir," I didn't want him to think I was hiding something.

"Alright. So, Sergeant Lovelace, you agree to answer my questions now fully and honestly?"

"Yes, sir," I said, raising my voice to satisfy him.

"You and Senior Airman Tobias went on a camping trip to Devil's Den Park and Nature Preserve in northern Arkansas. That wildlife preserve is federal land. Did you know that?" he said in an ominous voice, emphasizing "federal land."

"No, sir." But I thought, so what? What's the big deal?

Gregory asked, "Did you and Tobias stay at the park last night?"

"No, sir," I said in the belief he was referring to the campgrounds and not the park in general.

Gregory went ballistic, "Like bloody hell! Then where'd you stay … the Hilton? You didn't buy a camping permit and you didn't stay at the campgrounds! The park rangers found your abandoned campsite deep inside that nature preserve. If you're going to lie to me, I'll hang your ass, son!"

His face was red and the veins in his neck stood out. Many years later in retrospect, I think his rage was all theatre. He set me up by asking multiple questions requiring yes and no responses. It was one of his ways to assert dominance and establish who was in charge.

I said as earnestly as possible, "Yes, sir! I misunderstood. I thought by *park* you were referring to the campgrounds. No, sir, honestly! I misunderstood you. We didn't buy a permit and we didn't stay in the campgrounds either. But yes…we went into the wildlife area. All of the maps and directions showing where we went are still in the glove box of my car."

With a nod from Gregory, the captain stood up and left the room.

Agent Gregory knew I was sufficiently intimidated. He said, "Son, I'll let that slide one time because you just might be that damn stupid. The park rangers found your campsite. You left behind a blanket that was marked *Property of the USAF* alongside your government issue DEET and sunscreen. Your buddy left his little camera and a backpack with his name and address on it. It wasn't too hard to track you two down."

"I understand sir," I said. I was sure there had to be more to this story. I knew it had to do with what we witnessed and experienced in that damn meadow. This was about the thing we saw. I'll be damned if I'd tell him what we saw. I remembered what happened when I told people about seeing a flying saucer.

Gregory asked me with honest curiosity, "Son, there are a dozen state parks within an hour's drive or less from here. Why would you drive half a day to go camping for two nights?"

I explained, "Sir, Toby suggested Devil's Den. The location was his idea. I have a camera with a telephoto lens and a tripod. I hoped to get pictures of wildlife and some scenic shots. Toby is an amateur astronomer and he wanted to watch the stars. Devil's Den has some high ground. We found a summit in the preserve that gave Toby a good view of the night sky and it gave me panoramic scenery in all directions."

"So, you and your buddy trespassed into the nature preserve and set up a camp. According to Tobias, you guys saw some stars that looked funny. Then you just went inside the tent and fell asleep around midnight. Is that right?" he asked.

"Yes, sir," It sounded suspicious the way he phrased it.

He continued, "Then you got up and left at three o'clock in the morning. You got in your car and just left? Is that correct?"

"Yes, sir, I know that sounds odd."

"Did you plan on coming back the next day? That's the only reason to leave everything behind. Do you have a little marijuana plot out there or something?"

I was shocked. My mind was racing. What if someone had a little weed garden out there? That could mean very big trouble if they tried to pin it on us. "No sir, we didn't plan to come back for anything, and we sure didn't have any marijuana."

Gregory asked, "That's just odd. Don't you think? You two leave all your gear and abandon your campsite. Then after just three hours of sleep, you drive halfway across the state of Missouri?"

"Yes, sir, I guess it does sound crazy…sir."

Gregory shifted gears, "Crazy? You and your buddy saw some lights in the sky? Airman Tobias said you saw three lights that looked like stars. What did you see out there, son?"

"Sir, I saw the same thing. Three lights that looked like stars," I said.

Gregory asked, "How long did the two of you lay there and just watch these stars?"

"About three hours, sir."

Looking shocked he yelled, "Three hours! Now think real hard and tell me exactly how many photographs of these stars you took during those three hours?"

I replied truthfully, "None, sir. We just watched them and then went to bed."

Gregory looked puzzled. He said, "You what? You see something unusual and you didn't take a photograph? Everybody in your squadron says you're a photography nut and you didn't take a picture of something you thought was odd. Something Tobias said was almost over your heads?"

Now I was certain these guys had interrogated Toby. I had no way of knowing what he told Gregory and his sidekick. I tried to explain, "Sir, we just watched them for a couple hours and then we went to bed inside the tent. The stars were still up there when we turned in. We went to sleep around midnight."

Gregory scribbled some notes. After a long pause he asked, "Son, what were you planning to do on this trip exactly? You two want to look at the stars and take tourists pictures during the day? You could have stayed at the campground with hot showers and still have done all those things."

"Sir, I was hoping for some nature shots like wooded scenery and eagles."

Gregory asked, "And just how many shots of eagles and scenery did you take?"

"None, sir." It was obvious he didn't believe me. I could read it in his face.

"Let's try again, son! Tell me what you and Airman Tobias planned to do inside this nature preserve?"

"Sir, yes. We planned on hiking and doing some wildlife photography. I've got a 35mm camera with a good telephoto lens," I said. I felt uneasy now. I knew where this was headed, and I wasn't looking forward to telling him.

Sarcastically, Gregory asked, "So what do you photograph with this telescopic lens of yours when you're not trespassing onto federal land or bumbling around in a nature preserve?"

I wasn't even sure it was a question.

"Sir, it's a telephoto lens not a telescopic lens," I said. I immediately realized it was a mistake to correct him.

He was furious, "Tele-what-the-hell! For some reason you're just not going to tell me what you photographed… I need your camera and all the film."

"Sir, I can have my wife bring it…" He interrupted me and shook his head.

"Unless you have film and a camera hidden somewhere, forget it! We're conducting a raid on your home and car right now. So just tell me. Where's the camera and the film you took on the trip? All I need is that roll of film!"

"I left it at home, sir. It's sitting on my kitchen counter… unless my wife moved it. I didn't take a single picture because I forgot the goddamn camera." They're searching my home and my car? Did I hear him correctly? I asked, "Sir, you're searching my house and my car, right now?"

"Don't look so surprised, Sergeant Lovelace. You just signed a consent form. You gave us your permission. I want your film and the camera you took on the trip. We'll develop your film for you. I just want to see what you've been photographing with this telescopic lens of yours."

"Sir, I..."

I lost my train of thought as the captain came back into the room. He pulled up his chair and popped open his briefcase. Security policemen had already searched my home. They took my camera, film and all my prints. They took our car and scared the holy hell out of my poor wife.

From his briefcase, the captain retrieved Toby's hand drawn map and the tourist map we snagged at a kiosk. He handed them to Gregory, who put on his reading glasses and carefully inspected both for a moment.

Gregory placed them on the tray table in front of me and said, "Sergeant Lovelace, you're going to help me make sense of this. Explain these to me."

"Sir, that's the map Toby drew so we wouldn't get lost trying to find our way out of the nature preserve when it was time to go home. This is the tourist's map we picked up near the visitor's center. The hand-drawn map shows our route inside the nature preserve. It picks up where the park's map ends," I said.

"Show me," Gregory demanded.

I placed the two maps side by side and used his pen to point, "Sir, here's where we left the park. Then we crossed here and drove into the wildlife area. We looked for a good open place to set up camp. Here is the high plateau where we stayed. It's a big open field. I call it a meadow."

He handed me a blank sheet of paper from his legal pad, "Draw the shape of the meadow for me as if you were looking down on it from above. Then draw a line to show where you drove into the meadow. Got it?"

"Yes, sir." I said. It took just a second.

"Now draw a large arrow to point north and draw a little box where you parked the car. Try to keep it to scale as much as you can."

"Here sir, this area is all grass. Right here is where we parked my car and the arrow points north."

Gregory was pleased. His instructions continued, "Now draw a little circle where you set up your tent and show me where the tree line starts."

"Yes, sir."

"Now, estimate the meadow's length and width for me."

"Sir, I'm not good at estimating distance," I confessed.

"Just use the length of your car. Use the car like the scale on a map. Just give me your best estimate," he said.

It took a couple minutes. "This is it, sir." I handed back his pen and my drawing.

Gregory studied it and stuck it in his folder with the maps and papers I signed. Then he turned his attention to the captain again, "You get his camera and film?"

"Yeah, we got a 35mm camera. It had a fresh roll of film in it but no exposures. We seized three unopened boxes of film. All black and white and all are high resolution. One is infrared made specially for use in poorly lit conditions or at night. They were all bought at the base exchange. The receipt is in the bag. There was nothing there under his name for pick up, I checked."

Gregory turned back to me now, "Son, what kind of wildlife or scenic photography uses high resolution black and white film? What kind of scenery were you planning to photograph in the dark? You're going to have to explain that one to me too."

I did my best to explain, "Sir, I read a book from the library about Ansel Adams. He was a famous photographer 75 years ago. He's famous for his black and white prints of desert scenes and mountains. Black and white film makes high quality outdoor prints. I use it mostly to photograph eagles and the moon."

The captain rejoined the conversation, "We have every negative that was in the house. We got the wife's camera, it's a cheap 35mm. It was in a bedroom drawer with seven exposures. We're processing that roll now. It should be ready in an hour."

"Very good." Gregory smiled.

The captain continued, "Sergeant Lovelace has a darkroom set-up. It's in the rear bedroom. We took all the negatives and prints. He seems fascinated with the full moon for some reason. We've got a dozen prints or so here. I thought you'd find them interesting. But not a single roll of exposed film."

Gregory's response was harsh and immediate, "Sergeant, where's the film from your trip?"

"Sir, I left my camera at home! When we were in the meadow, I didn't have a camera."

"I don't believe you son, and that's a big problem. Do you get it? I think you have a roll of film stashed somewhere. I don't understand why you need a darkroom either. Why don't you develop your film at the base exchange like everyone else?" Gregory asked.

"Sir, it's a cheap hobby if you develop your own prints. Plus, you can crop and enlarge images in the dark room and do all kinds of things."

Gregory wasn't dumb, he knew that already. He had more knowledge about photography than he let show. Before Gregory could ask his next question, the nurse returned. She had a syringe in her hand and a look of determination on her face.

"Dr. Sanders wants Sergeant Lovelace to have his medication. I can bring the doctor down here if you like," she said with authority. OSI agents may be tough guys, but they're no match for a registered nurse.

"No need. I think we're about done here. I don't think Sergeant Lovelace has much more to add." He was annoyed by the interruption. The nurse gave me an injection and left.

Gregory turned his attention back to me. He didn't appear angry. He spoke calmly and asked, "Sergeant, where is the film? I need the negatives for every single photograph you took since you crossed the Arkansas border."

"Sir, I don't have any," I said.

Without telegraphing their move, both men abruptly stood and killed the tape recorder. They packed up their things and moved toward the door. I was relieved.

Before he left the room, Gregory told me, "You're being reassigned but you'll be staying at Whiteman. You'll be reassigned and work in a support section. Those orders will be cut today, but of course, that's all subject to change."

"Yes, sir." I thought, thank God. I get to finish my enlistment here, unlike Toby, and I'm not handcuffed to the bed.

Gregory continued, "You are ordered not to leave the base without permission from your CO or myself. You will not speak with Senior Airman Tobias or his family. You will not communicate with them in any way. That means no notes or letters. You will not discuss this incident with anyone at your new duty station or disclose the reason for your reassignment, are you with me, son?"

"Yes, sir. I understand."

He added, "Don't attempt to contact Tobias through a third party either. That means your wife or anyone else. You will not talk about the lights you saw in the sky that night. Not to anyone. That means not your wife, not your priest, or your mother, no one. Do you understand me?"

"Yes, sir. I understand everything," I said.

Then he paused. His demeanor changed and for a minute he just stared at me. Then he lowered his voice to a whisper, "You two knuckleheads stumbled onto something that made you very sick and I think you know what it was. Oh, I think you know what I'm talking about! Don't you son? I know you do."

"Yes…sir," was all I could add.

"If you come across that other camera or if you have something you want to tell me, just pick up the phone." He dropped a business card on my tray table. "There's my number, call me."

Then he smiled and even killed the overhead lights as he left. "Strange guy," I muttered as the door shut behind him.

A short while later my wife arrived. Tearful and overwhelmed by the raid on our home and our car being seized. I held her. I should say we held one another.

She had news too. "Tammy called me. They're being reassigned! They don't even know when or where. She told me not to call her or come over. She said it was an order."

Unbelievable! They sure as hell don't want us to compare our stories. To reassign Toby was just insane. To reassign me to a support unit was insane too, but far less harsh.

I couldn't reconcile my feelings. I didn't want anything to do with Toby or Tammy, ever. My feelings about Toby had changed. You'd think two people with a shared experience like this would be together and supportive of one another. It was the kind of event that bonds people. It wasn't supposed to distance us. But it did.

I gave her our good news, "I'm being reassigned to a support unit. That's a disappointment but I can finish out my enlistment here. I think the idea is to keep Toby and me separated until he ships out. Once he's gone, I'm hoping to go back to work in the ER."

She was relieved too. But she shared my anxiety.

"Terry, I know you probably want to say goodbye to Toby. But they warned us. We're not supposed to have any contact with them. I'm afraid of these OSI people. Please cooperate and don't piss them off."

"Sheila, I promise I'll cooperate with them. Don't worry, this will blow over. I promise."

My feelings about Toby had changed radically. I felt it in the car on our way home. I couldn't understand it. I felt relieved that Toby was leaving.

He's a bad memory gone. I didn't want to see Toby again ever, except for a quick goodbye and "nice knowing you."

I would see Toby one last time despite my feelings. I'd violate Gregory's order of no contact. I'd risk going to jail to say goodbye to a man I wanted nothing to do with? It made no sense.

As I was being discharged from the hospital, one of the doctors stopped by. It was the older doctor who wanted me to have the chest X-ray. He sat on my bed and told me what to expect after I'm released from the hospital and "clear-up some loose ends."

"Sergeant you're being reassigned to a support unit. They really don't have a spot for you yet, but they'll keep you busy I'm sure."

That was disappointing news, but Agent Gregory told me it was coming.

"Sir, why can't I just go back to work in the ER?"

"The higher-ups asked us to find you something else to do until Tobias is off base. You're not going to reenlist. You're just running the clock until your enlistment's up. Do you want to stay in the ER and work the nightshift again with a new partner?"

"Yes sir, I'm a good EMT and I love my job. I'm an asset to the squadron."

"Maybe when things settle down you can get back to us. Your CO was sorry to learn you're being reassigned. We'll see if we can get you back on an ambulance before your enlistment's finished. But meanwhile, I have a few things I want you to know."

"Yes, sir."

"Keep your nose clean and your mouth shut, and everything will be okay. Just stay out of trouble and you have nothing to worry about. Tobias told us you guys were drinking out there. The burns that you two suffered were from exposure to the sun and from naturally occurring radiation in the limestone bluff. You guys laid right on top of a uranium deposit probably with your shirts off. Now, the world doesn't need to know that. The red spots were chigger bites from lying in the grass and not using enough DEET. Understand, sergeant?"

"Yes, sir. Thank you. Now it makes sense." That made no sense at all. What kind of idiot does this guy think I am? That's the biggest load of crap I ever heard!

The doctor babbled on, "I want you to know, both you guys were pretty sick when you came back. Tobias got it worse than you did. We gave you some strong medication. It can cause you to have funny dreams and affect your memory. Even months from now, a funny dream might pop up. It's just a side effect from the medication. If you don't discuss them with anyone, they'll go away fast."

"Yes, sir. I understand." I'm not supposed to discuss my dreams? We must have seen something important. Something secret. They know Toby and I were abducted by aliens along with a score of other poor souls and used as lab rats. That was the only thing that made sense to me.

"Don't mess around with these OSI people either. You hear me sergeant?" the doctor added.

"Yes, sir, loud and clear. I understand and thank you, sir."

I was discharged from the hospital and sent home with a bucket full of pills along with strict instructions on how to take them. I asked Nurse Debra, "Hey Deb, what the hell are these pills? What are they for?"

She hesitated. "I'm not sure Terry. They aren't from our pharmacy…they were sent here from Wright Patterson," she said.

I knew Deb well. She wanted to tell me more but chose not to. Rank may have been an issue too. She wore a silver bar on her collar.

Every evening, they sent a nurse to our home. Her demeanor was formal, almost businesslike. She never once asked how I felt. It was her job to count the capsules to make sure I had taken my daily dose of nine. Three with each meal. They wanted to be certain I took them as directed.

These were odd generic-looking capsules. I worked in a hospital. I had a recent edition of a Physician's Desk Reference or PDR at home. The book has color photographs of every single capsule approved by the FDA.

These capsules weren't listed anywhere! That meant they were specially made by a pharmacist. But from Wright Patterson? What was their purpose? I wish I'd saved just one capsule.

Once I was home, my memory began to suddenly fail me. I couldn't remember the simplest things. I would misplace my watch and a dozen other things out of character for me. Even the day of the week was suddenly a mystery. Sheila was worried about my mental state. Then she made a connection.

Taking the capsules coincided with my rapidly deteriorating memory. I had taken just three of the fourteen days prescribed. Sheila deduced the capsules were the cause of my memory loss. I stopped taking them immediately and only saved enough pills to satisfy the nurse's evening pill count. I flushed three capsules down the toilet after every meal in case she came early I wanted the pill count to jive. That routine lasted eleven days. My memory improved in a week and fully returned in a month. I wonder if Toby had been poisoned by those capsules.

Our car was returned after just two days. It had been detailed beyond belief. My old Impala had not been so clean since it left the assembly line in Detroit. It had been scrubbed inside and out. We were grateful to have the car back, but I never understood why they took my car. At least not at the time.

A month after my release from the hospital, we drove past Toby's house. Not intentionally. We were on our way home from the grocery store and it was the most convenient way home. I was more concerned about running into Toby at the dry cleaners or the grocery store than at his home.

Sheila was driving, and we were two blocks from Toby's house. Despite being ordered to have no contact, I pleaded with Sheila, "Please, park so I can say a quick goodbye. I won't be a minute. I promise it'll be okay. I'll be right back."

Sheila was afraid to stop but relented when I begged. She pulled over and parked in front of Toby's house.

"Terry, hurry, please hurry," she begged.

There was a moving van in their driveway. Movers were busy hustling in and out with boxes almost at a trot. The front door was wide open.

"Sit tight, baby. Everything's fine. I just want a quick goodbye and I'm done." I gave her a peck on the cheek and walked up the short sidewalk to Toby's front door.

Without knocking, I walked inside like I'd done a hundred times before. I met Tammy just as she rounded a corner with a lamp in her hand. Surprised, she glared at me with a hard look. "You shouldn't be here." She kept walking.

She was angry. She probably thought it was my fault they were being uprooted so abruptly. I understood her anger. Maybe she was right. Maybe I'm responsible for whatever happened to Toby and this was all my fault somehow. Maybe that's why it was so important for me to see him one last time.

Toby heard our brief exchange, as he rounded the corner. He was shocked to see me. He looked like hell. An embrace seemed appropriate, but we shook hands. He said, "I guess you heard we're reassigned?"

This moment in my life, those few seconds are in my mind like the birth of my children. Not in a joyous way, but it was significant.

"I just want to wish you goodbye. I… wish you good luck…"

Toby looked me in the eye and said very softly, "Do you remember? Did it all really happen, Terry, all of it?"

Before I could answer Toby's question, Tammy brushed past us in the hallway again. I'm certain she intentionally interrupted our conversation.

I broke from his gaze and looked down at my shoes. Toby smelled of alcohol and his eyes were bloodshot. His question shook me to my core. Just seeing Toby again and hearing his voice triggered anxiety. I felt my heart pounding in my chest. I wanted to turn and run.

I knew what I had to say, and I owed him that much. I told him, "Yeah, it really happened, Tobe, all of it and they hurt us… I don't know why. But it's real, my brother. You're not going mad."

That was it. I never re-engaged his eyes. I turned and stumbled back to the car without looking back.

That was the last I would ever see of Toby. I had no way to know what lay ahead for him. Strangely, while I was attending law school 45 minutes away, Toby was dying on the streets of Flint, Michigan. Had I known, maybe I could have done something. Survivor's guilt?

I wish we could have reconnected. But Toby wasn't to be found. Sometimes people choose not to be found. Toby had vanished.

As I exited through Toby's front door, I was horrified to see that two security policemen in a marked car were parked out front. I had been inside for less than four minutes. They were parked right on our ass, too! There was a pick-up truck parked in front of us, so they had us boxed in. I hopped in the car. Sheila was in a panic and crying.

"What should I do? Oh my God, Terry they're going to arrest us!"

"No way. We'd be in handcuffs right now if they wanted us. You're going to calm down. You're a good driver, this is no worse than parking in downtown St. Louis. Just take your time and wiggle out of this space. Take us home, baby, you can do this. Just remember to be calm. They are still in their car. Just take a slow deep breath and you can do this."

I wasn't about to ask the cops to back up. When I saw their faces in the mirror, they were laughing at us.

Now calmer, Sheila slowly extracted us. She went forward and back a couple times and then we were free. We drove home. Our house was only a few blocks from Toby's.

The two cops rode our ass all the way home. They were literally inches from our rear bumper. Careful not to exceed the posted 20 mph speed limit, we crawled home. She hit her blinker and we pulled into the driveway. Sheila let out an audible sigh.

The cops parked at the curb directly in front of our house. They watched us.

I grabbed the groceries while Sheila unlocked the front door. I could hear the phone ringing. I dropped the groceries on the kitchen table, and I grabbed the phone.

"Hello."

"Hi, Sergeant Lovelace. This is Special Agent Gregory with the Office of Special Investigations." He sounded uncharacteristically pleasant.

"Yes, sir."

"Well, you just couldn't do it could you? You had to risk it all and violate a direct order from a superior officer. Violating an order is a serious offense, son. It really pisses me off when someone in uniform disobeys an order of mine!"

"I'm sorry, sir!" I wondered if the guys in the police car out front were going to arrest me. Maybe arrest both of us.

"You're just dying to exchange uniforms, aren't you?"

"Exchange uniforms? I don't understand, sir."

"Do you prefer your blue uniform, or would you like to exchange it for something with black and white stripes?"

"No, sir?" It took a second or two for his words to register. Then I knew what he meant. He was talking about a prison uniform.

"Son, what did you and Tobias talk about? What did you give him to keep for you? Did you find that other camera yet?"

"No, sir, and nothing, sir."

"Watch your ass, Lovelace. We're watching yours. I think you need a new hobby. Instead of photography how about stamp collecting? That would suit you."

Then he just hung up!

The security policemen sat in front of our home for about an hour. Then they left. Thankfully, nothing ever came of it. But every day afterward, I faced the worry of being arrested.

After the phone call from Gregory, I realized this whole thing was eating me up inside. I thought maybe if I offered to take a polygraph test, we could end this thing. I had nothing to hide, at least as far as a second camera and film. I hadn't photographed the things we saw. I didn't know it at the time, but it was a stupid idea that likely would have cost me dearly.

I fumbled through my wallet and found Agent Gregory's business card.

I called him expecting to get the switchboard, but my call went right to his desk. He answered on the first ring. "This is Special Agent Gregory."

"Good morning, sir, this is Staff Sergeant Lovelace. I just had a thought sir. I could take a lie detector test for you. Sir, I can prove I haven't hidden anything or done anything wrong except going into the…"

True to form Special Agent Gregory cut me off. He was blunt, "You got some film for me yet? I'm waiting?"

I didn't answer.

"Otherwise, there's nothing to talk about. The clocks ticking son and I got my own lie detector!" He must have slammed the receiver down. The conversation only raised my anxiety.

Recuperating at home gave me time to rest. At Sheila's urging, I sat down and journaled everything that had happened. I began with the start of the camping idea. Bits and pieces of my memory faded a little each day and it was a struggle to get everything on paper. It was a race to get it all down before it evaporated. It was difficult to grab a pen and paper when I just woke up from a nightmare screaming. I wasn't as disciplined as I thought. It was my wife's patient but firm resolve to see that whatever I saw in the dream made its way into the journal. Sometimes, it was only images. I drew them as best I could.

Then it was time to return to work. I reported to my new duty station on time and looking my best. I was pleased that my new commanding officer seemed like a reasonable guy, as officers go. He said, "We don't have a spot for you as a medic. We're a support unit. But our first sergeant's a good man. He'll keep you busy."

"Yes, sir, may I ask where I'll be assigned?"

"That will be up to Roy. Around here our first sergeant is known as Roy. Also, I am lifting your travel restriction effective immediately."

"Thank you, sir!" That was good news at least.

I was dismissed. I strolled down the hallway to the door marked, "First Sergeant, Roland Gilbert." I'd prefer Roy over Roland any day. I knocked once and was told to enter. His office was closet size. He introduced himself as, "First Sergeant Gilbert." Okay, I'll call the guy First Sergeant Gilbert until he tells me otherwise.

He was a rail thin man. His expressions and mannerisms could best be described as "cold fish." He was anything but welcoming. I wasn't expecting a welcome party. But I didn't expect to be treated like a pariah either. He told me I'd be working the day shift.

I guess since I had declined to reenlist, I would spend the rest of my time counting days on my calendar and drinking coffee. Anyone who has ever served in the armed forces knows how important coffee is to the overall running of things.

My new co-workers avoided me like a leper. Roy was sure to assign me to a task that kept me isolated from the rest of the squadron.

Sounding chipper now, Roy said, "Lovelace, I have a few things that need to be done. Follow me."

Without a word, we walked outside. Behind the main facility was a large garage. It was once used as a workshop of some kind. There was an old wood lathe in a corner and still sawdust on the floor. It had been a carpentry shop at one time. But it looked like it had been abandoned since the Korean War.

Handing me a key, he said, "Here is your key to the kingdom. Don't lose it. Lovelace, see that stack of plywood there?"

"Yes, I see it." Damn I wasn't blind, and I hated being addressed by last name.

"I need you to spray paint thirty 4x8 foot sheets of plywood. Paint both sides. Use the white paint in the corner and take your time. Do a good job."

I didn't question the purpose. My instructions continued.

"Lovelace, you can take an hour for lunch between noon and 1:00 p.m. Lock up while you're gone. At 4:30 you can call it a day and go home. I'm very busy. Let me know when you're done. Otherwise, I don't need to hear from you, understood? Just come and go as needed inside the shop. If you have any questions, now is the time to address them."

"No, sergeant. I think I got it."

Unbelievable. I was an exceptional EMT with skills learned by years of experience in the field. There were any number of productive things I could do. Now, I'm painting plywood? Maybe it was because I had Agent Gregory still on my ass? It didn't make sense. I'd come to expect things not to make sense.

The spray paint was old and very low quality. It took several coats of paint to cover the bare wood. It took weeks. When I was finished, and everything was dry, I reported to the first sergeant's office. I knocked on Roy's door.

"Lovelace! Come in. How's your project coming?" he asked.

"I wrapped it up today. Would you like to see?" I asked.

"Oh yeah, let's go see what they look like." His enthusiasm was disingenuous.

He walked with me in silence to the workshop. After 10 minutes of inspection he pointed out a spot or two where the paint had run. It really was insignificant.

"Very good, Lovelace. Not too bad."

"Thanks, sergeant. Do you have anything else I could do for the unit? Hopefully something a little more cerebral?"

He pretended to think for a moment, rubbing his chin, “Yes, yes I do. Now, strip them down to bare wood. Sand paper is on the workbench.” He turned and walked away.

I understood him loud and clear.

Hypnosis

Two months later, I was still in my workshop and diligently sanding away the same paint I had so carefully applied weeks earlier. I began to enjoy the privacy and now considered the old garage to be, "my workshop." I was surprised one day to see the first sergeant drop by to visit. That was a first. But he didn't come into the shop. He just yelled at me through an open door.

"Hey Lovelace! The CO wants to see you right away. Lock up here before you go."

Asking me to lock up the shop before leaving was troubling. That meant I'd be gone somewhere for a while. It was not a good sign. I locked up the shop and made a quick stop to take a leak. I looked in the mirror to check my appearance then ran down the hallway to his office. His secretary was waiting for me. She motioned me to go in.

"Sergeant Lovelace. Reporting as ordered, sir."

His office was decorated with the usual war souvenirs and self-aggrandizing photographs and awards. The tone of his voice was pleasant enough.

"Stand at ease Sergeant Lovelace. They want to see you at OSI headquarters. They've sent a car for you. It should be at the front entrance by now. I suggest that you don't keep them waiting. You are dismissed."

I made a quick exit.

This would be either very good or very bad. Breaking into a run, I headed down the long corridor to the front door. There was a dark blue squad car pulling up to the front stairs.

The driver opened the car's back door for me. He never said a word during the ten-minute ride to OSI Headquarters.

This was my first and last time in the back of a police car. I noticed there were no doorknobs, window cranks, or locks. The floor was steel with two metal rings bolted to the floor. I imagined they must be for securing shackled prisoners. The thought was chilling. The car smelt vaguely of vomit and that pine scented floor cleaner the hospital uses. The ride did nothing to ease my sense of dread.

The driver parked the car at the front entrance. Opening my door, he said, "Follow me."

We went up a few stairs and we were "buzzed in" through a pair of heavy steel doors. They made a metallic "click" when unlocked and again as they closed behind us. The place was intimidating. It was painted drab grey and muted pastels with very few windows. The building looked like something Stalin would design. Even the architecture was intimidating.

We made a right turn and walked down another long corridor. The hallway was lined with steel doors on each side. He opened the door of room "D" with a key.

"Someone will be with you shortly." The metal door shut like a bank vault. I didn't try the knob. I knew it was locked.

Looking around, I did my best to take in everything. The room was maybe 14 x 14 and painted beige. In the middle of the room sat a steel military issue desk from the 50s, and a matching heavy padded chair. Three light fiberglass chairs were placed in the corners for a total of four.

I sat in the padded chair and looked around. The steel door had a small glass window about 5 x 7 inches square. It was made of thick glass and reinforced with crisscrossed wires. An electric clock hung on the wall above the door. To my left was a two-foot square mirror. I reasoned the mirror had to be a two-way affair. Who'd care about grooming enough to need a mirror in a holding cell? I wanted to look at it closely. I wondered what I'd see if I'd cup my hands to block out the light and looked in. I didn't think it wise.

I made myself comfortable and took note that it was now 9:15 AM. I was scared and anxious. I was ever so thankful I stopped to piss before the ride over.

Not a single soul passed in front of my little window. That seemed unusual. Then hours passed. It was 10:00 and then 11:00. I believe the wait was intentional.

At last, just a few minutes before noon, I had company. The door opened, and I recognized Agent Gregory and the captain. There was no apology for making me wait. No civility. As usual they were just all business. The door locked behind them.

I don't believe they said a single word to me. Other than to make me surrender my comfortable chair in exchange for one of the fiberglass ones.

Gregory finally spoke to me. He was civil if not pleasant. "Well, have you found any film for us?"

"No sir. I don't have any," I said.

"It doesn't matter anymore. If you cooperate today, we might just close your file. Would you like that?"

I said, "Yes sir, whatever I can do to put this matter behind me."

"We should be done in a couple hours," Gregory replied.

A couple hours! I thought to myself. What the hell are we going to talk about for hours? I noticed their little tape recorder was being set-up by the captain again. It was on the table, but the little wheels weren't turning yet. Agent Gregory pulled a manila folder from his briefcase. He retrieved a piece of paper from it and handed it to me.

He told me to read it to myself silently first. Then I would read it out loud for the recorder. I read the paper silently. It was a rehash of the forms I'd signed in the hospital. Most of it was to waive whatever rights I had. Also, that I agreed my statements were made knowingly and voluntarily. The captain switched on the reel-to-reel.

Gregory asked me, "Are you ready to read it for the record now?"

I nodded.

He rolled his eyes and tapped the tape recorder with his pen. Its wheels were turning. I knew what he wanted.

We started over. "Sergeant Lovelace, you may begin when you're ready. Keep your voice up okay? Go ahead."

Script in hand I began, "I agree under penalty … the Uniform Code of Military Justice ..."

I was on autopilot again. I was simply processing written words. I spoke mechanically. I was careful to enunciate each word but without processing it fully for content. I didn't read it for substance. These were just words falling out of my mouth. Like spray-painting plywood boards.

As soon as I was finished, Gregory said a few words into the recorder. He began, "This is Special Agent Gregory …." He stated my name and gave the date and time, a file number, etc.

Then Gregory addressed me again, "Sergeant Lovelace, has anyone mistreated you or physically harmed you in any way?"

"No, sir," I was quick to reply.

"Has anyone threatened you or promised you anything in exchange for your statements today?"

"No, sir."

With that, he turned off the recorder and we sat! We were waiting for something. It was a short wait.

The men went about their business as if they were preparing for another person to join us. They shuffled papers and whispered back and forth. The topic was fishing.

Gregory said to me casually, "You're going to be hypnotized today and administered some medicine to help you remember everything clearly."

"Medication! Sir, what kind of medication? Sir, but why? I told you everything and I don't have any film!"

He glared at me. Pulling a piece of paper from his briefcase he slammed it down on the table in front of me. With his index finger he pointed, "Is that not your signature, son?"

"Yes, sir, just why...?"

"This is all the *why* I need." Gregory then slid it into his briefcase. He nodded to the captain and the tape recorder was running again.

Now, I was really frightened. I thought about withdrawing my consent or asking for a lawyer. But I knew those options carried risks. I didn't trust these guys. I violated Gregory's "no contact order" when I stopped by Toby's house. I committed a trespass too. I knew I was screwed.

I decided to ask, "Do you guys think I saw something secret?"

That question didn't register at all. The room fell silent. I think it was because the tape recorder was running again. They ignored my question completely. Both men scribbled on their legal pads.

A few minutes later a major tapped on the little glass window. The captain was closest to the door and let him in. He wore golden oak leaves but no nametag. I'd never seen him before. He carried a little kit with him. It looked like a shaving kit made of leather.

This major shook hands with the agents. It was obvious they knew one another. He then made Gregory relinquish his padded chair in exchange for a fiberglass one. He must carry more authority than Gregory. He glanced at the tape recorder to be sure it was running.

In deference to the major, the two agents pulled back from the table. The major pulled his chair next to mine. He encroached on my space. Even though he wore a broad smile, he was intimidating.

I wondered who the hell is this guy? Is he the hypnotist?

Once everyone had settled, he shook my hand warmly. With eye contact and that broad smile, he introduced himself with enthusiasm. "Hi, Sergeant Lovelace. It's very nice to finally meet you. I'm Major Brownfield."

He carried himself more like a therapist or a priest than a military officer.

"But just today you can call me Brad instead of Major Brownfield. Won't you please? That is my name."

I took that to be an order and not a suggestion. He continued, "Sergeant, just for our little visit today, can I call you Terry instead of Sergeant Lovelace?" He maintained eye contact and never stopped smiling.

"Yes, sir, of course." I replied.

Smiling, he softly scolded me for calling him "sir." He asked, "Don't you mean, yes, Brad?"

"Sorry, yes, Brad." It was weird speaking to a major so casually while in uniform.

"Tell me a little about yourself, where are you from?" he asked.

Then began a pleasant conversation. He claimed to know folks in St. Louis. He rattled off a few landmarks. I sensed he was seeking common ground.

When I spoke, he listened politely and kept his smile. He nodded now and then when appropriate. This polite chitchat went back and forth for a good while.

He actually did put me at ease a little. I learned that a kind human voice has an impact on people. Especially on people stressed or scared.

Even in this confined environment I didn't feel like I was being interrogated, not yet at least. Not by Brad. But I knew things would soon change.

Brad feigned a genuine interest in everything I had to say. After a while, that began to make me uneasy. My life just wasn't that interesting. He must have sensed my discomfort and abruptly switched gears.

"Terry, do you trust me?"

That question took me by surprise. Feeling caught off guard I gave the courteous albeit untruthful answer, "Yes, Brad, I trust you."

"Good. You can trust me, Terry. That's very good."

The whole exchange just felt creepy. We talked for another ten minutes about photography and cameras. I began to feel weirdly comfortable with him again. It was like I knew this guy from somewhere. But mentally I knew it was time to put my guard up. I didn't want to be disarmed by kind words.

While we were talking, he opened his leather kit. He laid a little towel on the table and meticulously arranged the contents of his kit on the towel. He wanted things arranged just so. What caught my eye was a hypodermic syringe already loaded with a yellow fluid. I thought it could be sodium pentothal or something of the like. The stuff you hear in movies referred to as, "truth serum."

He continued to smile and began humming softly to himself. There was a blood pressure cuff with stethoscope, alcohol swabs, and a bandage. There was also a foot-long piece of rubber tubing to use as a tourniquet to locate a vein. Whatever that yellow stuff was, it was intended for me.

"Terry, have these gentlemen explained to you we're going to hypnotize you today? You signed a consent form to undergo investigative hypnosis. It's a common tool."

"Yes, sir—Brad. But why?"

"It's no big deal, Terry. Hypnosis can help you relax and help you to remember details that you might have forgotten."

I didn't reply. It was like the guy read my mind.

Brad stopped smiling and his voice turned ominous, "Are you thinking about withdrawing your consent now?"

"No, sir, no, Brad."

Still wearing his stern affect the major added, "Hypnosis will tell us if you're intentionally holding back information. Now, you wouldn't do that, would you, Terry?"

"I wouldn't, Brad. I won't lie to you or to the agents."

"Terry, listen if there's anything in your statement that you want to change or if there's anything you've held back because it slipped your mind, we can fix it. Tell me now and we might just be done here today."

"Brad, I told the agents everything I know," I answered.

"Terry, this is your opportunity to finish this. If you need to make any corrections to your statement, it's a lot better to just tell me now and I can help you. Terry, this will end very badly for you if you've been lying to Agent Gregory. I'll ask these two gentlemen to step outside and we can have a private talk, whada-ya-say, hmm?"

The two agents stood.

"Sir, I told them everything truthfully."

The two agents sat back down.

I had no option but to roll with it. But was determined—I was determined to resist giving him full control of my mind. I would passively and covertly resist his hypnosis.

I thought I could keep a little compartment in my mind segregated, separate. I tried to establish boundaries in my mind. I would wall off an area for the interrogation and an area for my conscious resistance. I won't let him hypnotize me! I told myself. I would resist but I knew I had to appear compliant at the same time.

Pushing the envelope, I spoke up one more time. "Now, I understand the hypnosis, Brad, but what's the injection for?"

The major raised his voice. Both agents jumped. He took on the stern affect again, "My goodness! For someone who claims to trust me you sure have a lot of questions!" He turned the smile back on, "Terry, it's just to help you relax. It makes the hypnosis process quicker and more effective. You'll feel like you've had a couple beers. It will help you to fully relax so you can remember things easily. Who knows? Maybe you'll remember something important that you forgot."

I didn't respond.

"Terry, I've done these a hundred times, and I promise you, this won't hurt a bit."

The discussion was over. He reached over and took my left arm. Humming all the while, he unbuttoned my shirtsleeve and rolled it up. With the rubber tubing tightly around my bicep, he began looking for a vein.

I watched him go about his business. I was more curious than afraid.

Chipper than ever, Brad said, "In a few seconds I'm going to give you a little injection in your arm here. I promise it won't hurt. It's very much like the medication they gave you while you were in the hospital. Now, do you still trust me, Terry?"

I lied, "Yes, Brad."

"Good." He took the cap off the syringe and held it in his right hand. "Now Terry, we've only just met, but I promise you I'm not going to hurt you in any way. A lot of people tell me they enjoy this experience. I bet you're a guy who enjoys a few beers on occasion." He followed up with a wink of his eye.

I said nothing. I was insulted. Not all enlisted guys drink.

"Just sit back now and listen to my voice. It's important that you don't resist the feeling. Let the medicine do its job. Obey the commands I give you and we'll be done before you know it. Will you do that for me, Terry?"

I had to reply aloud, "Yes, Brad. I promise." I thought, oh no, he's going to give me a hypnotic suggestion to obey his commands. I'd been taking evening classes in psychology for two years now. I knew a little about hypnosis and hypnotic suggestion. I knew it was possible to resist but the drug concerned me. I thought, if it were possible to drug a person into revealing the truth why would we need courts of law and trials? That thought gave me hope.

"Terry, have you ever been hypnotized before?"

"No, Brad."

I had some things to hide. But I sure as hell wasn't hiding any film. Some memories were so incredible I wanted to keep them to myself for fear they'd think I'm insane. Those incredible things I saw. I owned them, and I held onto them as validation. It was like when I tucked the curtain inside the venetian blinds in 1966. I didn't want to be robbed of the experience. Even if it was a bad experience. I owned those images the same way I owned my photographs. They were mine.

"You have a good vein here," he mumbled while he smacked the crook of my arm a couple times.

The major had a voice like a radio announcer, smooth and easy to listen to. He found a vein and scrubbed it with an alcohol swab. He cautioned, "Here we go. A little sting," smiling all the while.

"Listen to my voice, Terry, and forget about everything else now and just relax… relax."

I didn't feel a thing. Peeking through my mostly closed left eye I watched the needle pierce my arm. After he stuck me, he pulled back the plunger. A bit of blood backed up into the syringe. He had hit a vein.

I think Brad saw my eyelids flutter as I was peeking at the needle.

"Close your eyes now, Terry. Relax and keep your eyes shut and listen to my voice. That's better; you have good veins. Thank you, Terry."

Strange that someone would compliment the quality of my veins. I felt obliged to reply in kind. "You're welcome, Brad." I noticed the silence in the room. The agents were uncharacteristically quiet.

I heard "snap" and felt him remove the rubber tourniquet. I felt a flush and then warmth as my muscles involuntarily relaxed. Brad was correct. It was a pleasant feeling.

"There, all done. Terry, that wasn't so bad, was it?"

He placed a bandage on my arm.

I slid from feeling relaxed into feeling sedated. The acoustics in the room abruptly changed. This was not at all the same drug they gave me in the hospital. This was something very different.

"Terry, you're just going to feel a little sleepy, but you don't want to fall asleep. You want to listen to my voice. You're in a safe place. You feel warm and comfortable now."

At that instant I felt another wave of warmth wash over my body. I didn't feel like I was in that safe place though. I also reaffirmed in my mind that I would passively resist surrendering to Brad's voice.

I didn't "feel" hypnotized yet. I just felt sedated. His voice was well, hypnotic. I kept playing Beatles songs in my head. I did anything I could think of to avoid surrendering total control.

I didn't know how one was supposed to feel under hypnosis. But I didn't feel like I imagined one would feel. I'd seen people hypnotized on television programs using "stage hypnosis." I thought, I can mimic that kind of behavior, sleepy and robotic-like.

He continued in his monotone voice. "You're safe now, Terry, and we're going to go back in time together just to look around. I'll be right beside you. Would that be alright with you?"

"Okay, Brad, yes." I let my head droop to my chest and kept my eyes closed.

"Now listen carefully, Terry, and do as I say. I'm going to count out loud down from ten to one. I want you to imagine a stairway in your mind. Can you see a stairway leading down to a cellar?"

"Yes, Brad," I did have a mental image of a stairway.

"With each number I count, you'll take one step down on those ten imaginary stairs. You'll feel more and more relaxed with each step. You'll be relaxing more and more, more with every step you take as you listen to my voice. Just listen to my voice. Okay, Terry? Here we go."

He began his countdown.

"Take that first step, Terry, and feel relaxed. With each step you take, you'll feel twice as relaxed. You're warm and safe. I won't let anything hurt you."

The idea occurred to me as Brad's count continued downward, I can mentally count upward. I'll go the opposite direction on the number line. I'd climb up the stairs on the number line instead. I guess math class was good for something. I tried it mentally. It was the best idea I could come up with.

Brad continued, "Take the second step now twice as relaxed. You are relaxed and at ease, warm and secure."

I made the conscious effort to not relax all my body. Intentionally, I tightened the muscles in my toes and other parts of my body where he wouldn't notice I had tensed. I knew I needed to appear relaxed. But the smooth tone of his voice made me want to listen to him. I knew that was the danger, giving him my full attention.

We continued our opposite journeys on the stairway. "You're doing well, Terry. We're all very proud of you. Feeling eight times more relaxed now."

In my mind's eye, when he called off a step, I mentally took a step in the opposite direction on the mental stairway. I was headed away from that dark cellar. I'll stay upstairs in the light thank you very much!

I finished my count at #1 as he finished his count at #10. I was relaxed but conscious of my surroundings. I was aware of everything going on around me. But I felt very sedated.

"Ten. You're at the bottom now. Terry, above you there's a chain hanging down from the ceiling. I want you to reach up with your right arm and pull it downward to turn on the light, so we can look around. Do it now, Terry."

My arm didn't move on its own accord. I had complete control of my arm. I wasn't sure what to do. A few tense moments passed.

Brad tried again, "Terry, reach up now. Take the chain and pull it to turn on that light so we can look around a little."

This time I intentionally reached up with my right arm and made a motion like I was pulling a chain. I was pulling a chain alright. I was pulling Brad's chain. I then lowered my arm into my lap.

"It's brightly lit now, you're not in the darkness and you're very safe. Listen to my voice and relax, Terry."

I heard the captain whisper, "I'm amazed every time I watch this."

After a few minutes of whispering back and forth, I heard Agent Gregory ask in a whisper, "Is he under?"

The major replied, "Oh yeah, piece of cake… he was under before I hit three."

The captain chuckled.

I thought, so the captain is amazed every time he watches one of these? Damn, how many people do they hypnotize? They can't do this with everyone who sees a UFO? But my interaction was a little more intimate. I had established a dialogue with at least one alien being. I could see her clearly in my mind now. This is a familiar memory but one I hadn't thought about in a very long time. The medicine opened a doorway. It was as if you were trying to remember a word or phrase and someone gives you a hint. Then boom! You remember. I was remembering.

There was some hushed talk between the three about golf. I guess the major didn't fish. I was stunned. Surely, I wasn't supposed to hear this conversation.

The major asked one of the agents, "Let me review his cover sheet really quick." There was a shuffling of paper and a minute later I heard Brad say, "Alright, I got it, thanks, Greg."

Brad turned his attention back to me. "Terry, you can hear my voice. Do you feel nice and relaxed now? Okay, we're going to take that little trip back in time like I promised. Just to look around."

"Yes, Brad," I answered, anxious as hell.

"Good. You're a very good subject. You're the best subject I've seen in a while."

I just said, "Thank you." Like complimenting me on the quality of the vein in my arm; that must be a part of the process.

That felt eerie. It was awkward. I was in a pleasant twilight though. I was very relaxed but still aware of everything going on around me. It seemed to be working for me to split my mind into two separate compartments. I ran through the lyrics of "Yellow Submarine" and "Norwegian Wood."

"Now listen to my voice, Terry. Do you still trust me?"

"Yes, Brad, I trust you." Like hell, I thought.

"Terry, we're going to go back in time but only in your memory. We are only going there to look around before we get rid of those nasty images. Think of it like watching a movie. It seems real but it's just memories. They are things that happened a long time ago, not dreams or stories, but what you saw. I want you to tell me what you see. Let's go back to the meadow. When I tell you to, look around in your mind and tell me what you see."

"Yes, Brad."

"Nothing in your memory can hurt you, we are not going to let anything happen to you. I'm right here, and anything that's scary is just a memory."

That made me feel anxious. Sure, there are things I don't want to look at. It's like viewing an autopsy. Ugly and gruesome, not something to dwell on or even think about when it's over. Like snakes, some things are best to let lie undisturbed.

Brad could tell I was anxious. He reached out and took my right hand. He said, "Terry, hold my hand. Do you feel my hand?"

"I feel it, Brad," it was very strange holding this strange man's hand. But I admit it felt reassuring, too. If they surfaced, I expected there were memories that would be difficult to relive. He wanted me to be ready for the ugly when it came. We both knew it was coming.

Brad spoke to me like I was a child. It seemed weirdly appropriate at the time. I was beginning another song in my mind. It was playing in that private compartment where I maintained control.

"Now, I want you to think back. Do you remember taking a camping trip? Did you and Tobias go on a little camping trip?"

"Yes, Brad, it's Toby not Tobias. We went on a camping trip."

"Of course, you did. That's right! You and Toby went to Devil's Den. My, that must have been exciting! Tell me about your trip. Think hard and tell me what you see."

Throughout the entire interrogation, I felt conscious but very drowsy. There were times when I fell asleep for just a second or two only to have Brad pull me back.

I told Brad my edited version of the story. I told him about the drive, the girl in the store and crossing the chained area .... arriving at the meadow. How we chose a place to park in the meadow, the hike and falling asleep on the ledge. I told him about our mad dash to get back to the campsite before sundown. I gave a detailed account easily because I could watch it play out in my mind in sequence of events. It truly was like watching a motion picture in your head.

"That's good, Terry. I want you to tell me what you saw in the sky, if anything, when it got dark."

"Brad, there were three stars. We watched them travel from the horizon until they were directly over our heads. We were parked in the right spot..."

I must have been prattling on. There were times that I may have been under or asleep. Brad dragged up things from my subconscious mind. These were either things I had forgotten or things they repressed. These were the ugly things. Some of these things will sound outrageous I know. But in the introduction to this book, I promised I would tell you the truth. This is the truth. These were my objective experiences. Nothing here is subjective. I don't draw any conclusions.

Brad broke into my thought. "Tell me, Terry, how did you know just where to go?"

For some odd reason that question hit me like a slap in the face. "Brad, they told Toby where we should go. He knew right where to go. Toby knew. They didn't tell me, just Toby."

"Who was it, Terry? Who told Toby where to go?"

Without hesitation I spat out, "The space people did."

Did that just come out of my mouth? I was answering questions before thinking about my answer. I remembered the space people now. I had all but forgotten so much. I had forgotten a hell of a lot.

Here is where things get fuzzy. I'm aware and can hear my spoken responses to his questions. I don't recall thinking about the answers before they came out of my mouth. I tried to keep the door to the other compartment in my mind open by playing song after song mentally. I resisted with everything I had. But I felt a piece of me slip away now and then. Resisting hypnosis was very possible. Battling the effects of the drug was another matter altogether.

I told Brad, "Yes, in the meadow. Toby knew right where to park."

Brad paused, “Tell me all about getting to the meadow.”

“We found the correct spot to camp. It was on the edge of the meadow. We couldn’t go to a public campsite. We had to be up high on the plateau because that’s where they land.”

“Good, Terry. Tell me everything that happened that night. Did they take you and Toby together?”

“Yes and no, Brad. They took me twice. Toby slept through the first time on the rock ledge where we stopped to rest. Then they took me again late at night when they took me for a second time with Toby. They took blood from me and my sperm too. They have a machine they put over my genitals and bam. It’s humiliating but it was no good to resist them. They had us, Brad.”

I was seeing this play out in my mind. It was all familiar. These were real and terrifying memories suppressed by the aliens. I knew there was some scary things coming too. I had to appear relaxed but hold onto my grasp of consciousness. Now, I wanted to know what happened to us on that goddamn meadow. All of it.

I was quiet for a moment. Brad didn’t like it. He pressed me.

“Ah, Terry, you and Toby saw some lights in the sky. Didn’t you see some stars too? How many stars did you see?”

“Stars… three stars that formed a triangle. We watched them from where they sat on the horizon and followed them. We watched them go all the way up until they were right over our heads. The closer it got, the bigger it got… and it was very big.”

“Terry, did you know who it was? Who was in the meadow to visit you that night?”

“I told you, Brad. It was the space people.” I was annoyed.

Here is where I must have dozed off for a moment. There are gaps in the story here that I can’t account for.

"Yes, Brad, the space people. They wanted both of us this time. They hurt us too. They hurt me badly and they hurt Toby even worse. Much worse. I heard his screams."

Brad asked, "Tell me about the space people."

"I already knew the space people. I knew them before this night. I remember in the tent, Toby's voice saying to me, 'It was the space people, they took you too!' I remember. I said, 'Yeah, Toby. They took us both.' They took me when I was a little kid too. It was the monkeymen."

Brad was intrigued, "Terry, who are the monkeymen?"

Fear overtook me. I could see them clearly now. I saw them in my mind's eye. I softly sobbed as I saw the monkeymen for the first time unmasked. These were no friendly little monkeys. These were non-human entities disguised to fool a child and put them at ease.

"Brad, I know them. They came into my bedroom when I was little. They took me somewhere and there were toys and other children for me to play with. There was a lady there who was nice." I squeezed the major's hand. I knew I wasn't in danger, but all the emotions were there. I felt the same panic.

"Terry, you're safe. I'm right here. Now go on, continue."

I was reliving the horror of an alien abduction. It was both terrifying and familiar. I've known these space people all my life! I never thought of it that way before.

I told Brad, "They were the monkeymen from my childhood and they follow me. They always know where to find me. You can't hide from them."

"Terry, what do the monkeymen look like? Why do you call them monkeymen?"

"What an asinine question, Brad!" I shouted out loud. "Because they looked like little monkeys. There were four of them and they all wore masks. I can see them now; their masks are off. These aren't monkeys at all. These are the little grey people. They took me! They took me to play when I was little. Oh, God help me. I am so afraid of them. I can see their evil grin! They tricked me!"

"Okay, Terry, stay focused. Go back to the tent. What happened to you and Toby in the tent? Tell me what you saw?"

"We were taken from the tent," I said.

Brad asked, "You and Tobias saw the stars first? Then the triangle, and what did you see next?"

"We watched the ship come in from just three little lights. It climbed up and over us. God, it was so big. But we weren't afraid. Toby wasn't scared either. We just went to sleep. We were so tired, and we just weren't interested," I was reliving the whole thing in my mind and it was terrifying.

I could hear the major addressing the two agents, "I've seen this dozens of times before. There is alien apathy and alien amnesia. They're two separate phenomena. It's common."

I thought to myself, "alien apathy and alien amnesia," now I get it! It's why I went back to bed as a child with a spaceship parked outside my bedroom window. It's why Toby and I just went to sleep! I must remember this, it is important.

The major resumed the interrogation, "You weren't interested, and you went to bed. What time did you enter your tent that night?"

"Right before their ship docked. It landed in the field about midnight. But it was never on the ground. It stayed about thirty feet over the meadow floor. Brad, it just hung there," I said as I watched it all play out in my head. I was amazed at the images I saw, but they were familiar too. It was like seeing an old friend you'd not seen in years.

Brad said, "Terry, tell me about the spaceship in the meadow. What did it look like? What did you see?"

"A giant triangle of a spaceship. It was hundreds of feet across. It was huge, it was so incredible, I can see it now!" It was as fresh in my mind as what I had for breakfast. It was right there. I wanted to remember it and watch it some more. I paused. I saw it all again and I wanted to imprint it in my memory forever. I said, "It was right there, and it was so big! It filled the meadow like a five-story building."

"Good, Terry. That must have been exciting for you. Tell me about the ship. When they took you and you were inside with Toby, what did you see inside?"

"Incredible things. This had to be one of their bigger ones," I added almost as a matter-of-fact.

My conscious mind stopped playing the music. It dawned on me. He knows all about them already. He is spot on with everything. It was no star. The son of a bitch knew it was no star, it was a goddamn spaceship. How did he know? How could he know? He's leading me down a path to find out how much I know.

"Go on, Terry, you're doing well now what did you see?"

I spoke again without first composing my thoughts, "It was a big ship, Brad, a large one. It was different than the flying saucers and the giant ship I saw before. It wasn't silver, and it wasn't shiny. It was matte finish I'd call it and very dark grey or black. Kind of like the black diamond we saw over Kilo-5. It had lights on each corner that ran from the bottom to the top."

"Go on, Terry," Brad encouraged.

I was agitated again, "Brad these space people capture me and do terrible things to me … and then erase my memory! It happened when I was a little boy. But it wasn't just two times either. Oh God, they took me. They took me lots of times and made me forget it all. But they wanted me to remember just a little when I was a kid. So, I would recognize them when I grew up. I was programmed to see them as my space brothers, and I had to keep their secret."

"Good, Terry." There was a pause and shuffling of papers.

As a prosecutor, I learned how child molesters "groom" their victims. They ingratiate themselves into the victim's families to gain their trust. It took until now for the mask of my abusers to come down. I had been groomed. Those were terrifying but brief encounters in my childhood. But they were not nearly as brief as I remembered. They damaged my soul the way a child molester robs children of their innocence. There was so much I'd forgotten until Brad came along. He brought all this out again. He ripped the scab off my wound.

The drugs he gave me, and his faulty hypnosis brought it all back into my conscious mind. It was a eureka moment for me. An epiphany. I kept it to myself. What else has happened to me that I'm not even aware of? I heard someone once say, "You don't know what you don't know." I never understood the meaning of the phrase until that moment.

Suddenly, I was angry with Brad. I was really pissed-off. I tried not to let it show. I spoke up, "There are some things we're not supposed to talk about, Brad! I'm not supposed to talk about them. You know that! It's a secret and there are consequences if you disobey them. They'll make us both pay! We're in danger now!"

That caused quite a stir. Evidently Brad's the one asking questions and my commentary wasn't appreciated. Brad shot back quickly and reassuringly to calm me down and take back his role as the inquisitor, "No, no it's alright! They gave us permission. Terry, you're safe now. They won't be mad at you! I promise. They said it was alright for me to talk to you."

This attempt to calm me down had the opposite effect. He had permission? Who, in the chain of command gave him the authority to speak on behalf of the aliens? A USAF major had permission? That shook me up. I didn't believe it at first because it was so incredible. I felt myself slipping again. Mentally, I busied half of my mind with Brad while the other half was reciting the multiplication tables. Trying to hold onto a piece of consciousness.

Brad interrupted my thoughts, "Wake up! Stay focused on the triangle. Terry, tell me what you're seeing now."

"Brad, I told you. It was a big, goddamn triangle. As big as the whole goddamn meadow. That's why we had to park by the tree line, so they had room to park over the meadow."

I must have dozed off again at a critical juncture or at least I think so. My memory of this event is not a seamless narrative.

Brad's voice startled me, "Go on, Terry, and tell me what you see."

Disturbed by the unaccountable period, I began again, “It was black and five stories tall. It was enormous. There were three saucers situated inside like planes on a carrier parked below deck. There was a crowd of people too. We’re all waiting for our turn on the table. The space people control us. The taller aliens are milling about. They are the ones who control everything. If one of them looks at you it’s like being naked. They can see and know everything in your mind. That was the scariest thing, so I avoided looking at them.”

“How many humans did you see?”

“Fifty or sixty. A lot of people… some of the human beings were crew members. They ignored us.”

“Tell me, Terry. Tell me what the human crew members wore?”

“Tan colored flight suits with orange insignias of rank on their shoulders,” I said. That created a stir. I heard Gregory say, “Son of a bitch.”

“Terry, you’ll forget about the men in tan flight suits. Tell me, where did they take you next?” Gregory wanted to know. In retrospect I think he wanted to shift my focus away from the men dressed in tan.

“They marched us past a long wall of aquariums. I don’t want to look at them, so I turn away. They’re dreadful things, you know Brad? They do horrible things there,” here was the ugly. I knew it was coming.

“Terry, turn your head now and look. Terry, tell me about the aquariums… what do you see?”

“They are big fish tanks. Inside them… I thought they were puppies at first… reptilian lizard-like things floating in pink water. They were ugly with big eyes. One twitched!” I must have screamed.

Brad forced me to look, “Terry! They’re images from the past and they can’t hurt you now! How many aquariums did you see?”

“A hundred or more aquariums… they cover a whole wall. There is pink water inside and some are bigger. They look like… no, hell no! These are human beings? How can this be? These can’t be living human beings … they are different. Oh god, they are not like us! One moved again, its head turned toward us, and its eye blinked!" Startled, I screamed, "For God's sake, no!"

I must have fainted. I was overwhelmed. I felt my heart pounding. In my mind I turned away and tried to think of other things. I tried to think about good things like flowers, butterflies, "Norwegian Wood," the love of my wife, and things of beauty. Not these goddamn monsters that Brad made me see again.

I heard the familiar zzzzzzzip, of a blood pressure cuff. Brad was taking my blood pressure and reminding me, "Terry, you're here now and you're safe. That was in the past. Squeeze my hand."

I squeezed Brad's hand and just like before, I felt grounded again. I felt safe. I'm going to remember this for the rest of my life, I swear to God I will. I'm not going to let him rob me of these ugly memories and thoughts. No matter what… I will not forget this!

Then a disturbing thought. They wouldn't allow a lowly NCO to know about this stuff. So why help me remember? They want to know how much I know… how much I've seen… they want to know if I have photographs too.

I didn't trust these guys. I could be killed in an accident of their design. I could be falsely imprisoned with some made-up story of photographing restricted nuclear facilities or cultivating a marijuana plot in the nature preserve. Any number of things could be engineered to silence me. I remembered the old senile doctor who saw me as I was being discharged from the hospital. He warned me, "Don't mess around with these OSI people." But that was exactly what I was doing, and I was afraid for my life.

"Tell me what happened next, Terry. What else did you see inside the craft?"

"We all walked by the aquariums. Now we're just waiting our turn in a big room. Everything is white or steel. Some people are nude and holding their clothes."

Brad was back in control. The music had stopped playing once more. I was strolling around this spacecraft with a small woman. I could see her. I knew her, and I tried not to tell Brad about her. Maybe I did. Brad asked again, "Tell me about this spacecraft and what you saw."

"I had never seen a triangle before. I've been in their ships before. Even bigger ships. I was inside of one so big it can never land here because it is as big as a city. I was taxied there and back in a saucer. I remember being inside a saucer and it was incredible. We shuttled back and forth in one. They were short trips that only took a couple minutes. There was a slight sensation of motion. It was like being in an elevator."

"Terry, tell me about the biggest one. The one bigger than the triangle. Tell me about that one. But only tell me what you see and what you were told if anything."

I was speaking on autopilot again. I was seeing things play out and then relaying to Brad, "It was an entire city a hundred times larger than the triangle. It was so different. On Earth there is a curve, so the horizon is as far as you can see. It's flat inside and I could see as far as my eyesight allowed. The depth of field made it almost like a 3D movie scene. I could make out people walking further away from us. There were probably hundreds of these compartments on either side of a long central corridor. There were golf cart things to move people around. It was like a highway down the center..."

I stopped talking to watch the images play out. Brad didn't like it. But it was captivating, I wanted to watch it.

"Terry, tell me what you're seeing now. Tell me."

"The tall ones... the aliens are milling about. There are walkways that move like at the airport. We were near the moon that time. There were huge windows and I could see the moon below us. It was dark, but I could see cities below that were lit up. It was a huge city on the surface of the moon. They go there for a special kind of rock."

"Go on, Terry. You're doing very well."

"The woman told me they can never fly in front of the moon... the side that faces Earth. It's because the ship is so big it could be seen from Earth."

"By whom, Terry? By people using telescopes?"

"Hell, no Brad! You could see it with two eyes! It would be a black dot traveling across the face of the full moon. Maybe that's why I like the full moon so much, do you think so, Brad?"

Brad was struggling to keep me on track, "Who was the woman inside the very big ship, Terry?"

"I don't know her name. We walked together for a while. We talked with our minds. They don't speak but it's easy to communicate. We can hear each other just like we're talking now. She told me the size of the ship but in kilometers. We're supposed to learn metrics now. She told me it was five hundred and some kilometers long and seventy-five kilometers tall."

"Did they tell you where they come from? Tell me what she told you."

"Yes! They stay on the other side of the moon but it's not their real home. It's not where they come from. They come from a place very far away; they have two suns and a couple moons. They never have nighttime so it's easy to grow things there. She told me it was very beautiful. I asked if I could go there but she said it wasn't allowed."

"Did she tell you anything else about our moon?"

"She said we have people living there too. Humans on the moon… for years now. I never knew that, Brad. I would never have imagined it." I said.

That caused a stir. I could hear whispering and pages of paper being flipped.

Brad was quick to jump in, "Very good. Go ahead, Terry, but you will forget that memory forever. You'll forget all about the moon, everyone knows there are no people on the moon, Terry. All about the big ship and the moon you will forget. It's gone now."

I didn't reply. And I don't think I forgot a goddamn thing either. I know what I saw. I remember what she told me.

As if on cue, Brad asked, "What else did she tell you?"

I paused, "I… I'm fond of her but not in a romantic way. Like I feel about my friends and people I like. I liked her. She said she was half human and half alien. She said there were a lot of them just like her… and more every day. I felt drawn to her. But my affection for her was maternal. She called me by my name and that helped me to feel more at ease. She was not pretty, Brad. But I knew her from before when I was little. She was so kind to me when I was so afraid. We hugged one another. My God… she's so thin and so fragile."

"What happened after you embraced?" Brad asked.

"The flap of her gown was open a bit and I peeked inside where her breasts would be. I think it's natural curiosity, but… I'm repulsed, it wasn't right Brad. It was not a human body. She was not a human being. It was ugly. She was not a real woman, but I felt fond of her. She talked to me. She kept me from being so scared when I was little, and they hurt me. It was good to see her again. Her kind words helped me to feel less afraid."

I was quiet for a while or there is a big gap here. I don't know which. I recall being startled again by Brad's voice, "Terry, what else did she say to you?"

I was apprehensive again. I knew I was not supposed to talk about this, "Brad, she said I shouldn't tell, and she made me forget. Did they really give you permission? Do you know them?"

That seemed to get everybody's attention. I had asked Brad a second question. The topic was off limits, I guessed by their response. Our roles were clearly defined. He was the inquisitor and I was his subject.

There is more hushed whispering. In my mind, I'm still trying to process my encounter with the alien woman. I was shocked and embarrassed that I admitted being fond of her. I was dumbfounded by the things I saw and the things I said. I was still processing the amazing images of her and of being aboard the huge spaceship. So many memories came flooding in… it was overwhelming. I needed to rest for a moment. I felt my heart pounding.

I felt a tightness around my left arm. Brad was checking my blood pressure again. I believe they were freaked out because I had questioned Brad. I needed to remember to not do that in the future, not to tip my hand. But I wasn't always able to control what came out of my mouth. I don't know how much time had lapsed but I was asleep for minutes at least.

"You're a good subject, Terry, and we're all proud of you. Do you still trust me?" asked Brad.

"I trust you." It came out of my mouth because I forced it to come out. I didn't trust this son of a bitch. I held onto my stubborn resolve not to allow Brad to take total control.

"Terry, we're going to go back one more time okay? Just once more and we'll be done."

I was worried about what I might have said during those moments I couldn't account for. I didn't know what happened during the times I lapsed into sleep or some trance state. The gaps worried me. I was seated away from the clock on the wall. Even if I were facing it, I couldn't lift my head to check the time. It felt like an hour had passed. It was more like four.

Brad took me on one more trip, "Okay, Terry, you're safe. I want you to go back once more and tell me what you see. What do you see?"

I was emotional. I said, "I was in the tent and I'm screaming. Although I'm not making audible sounds. I fill my lungs with air and screamed again but nothing came out. Everything was silent except for that incredible hum. It was dark except for some bright lights that occasionally flashed outside the tent. Toby was gone."

"Did they take you again, Terry?" Brad asked. Of course, he knew they took me again.

"The second time… I was in the tent and the lights were so bright. The humming got louder, then there's that twirling spin. We go right through the tent into the triangle from the center below it. I saw the flash of white light and then I'm in a giant room with other people." I remember a long pause before getting back on topic, "The little grey people are undressing everyone. I was waiting… then they took me into that damned white room. I've been there before, Brad. I'm on their table and held down. Then I can't move at all."

Brad wanted to know, "Do they use straps to hold you down to the table?"

"Never, you're just immobile. I didn't know where Toby or the other people went. I could hear a woman screaming now. The sadness of her scream! Brad, it was dreadful!"

"What do you see happening next, Terry?"

I didn't answer. I was just watching the images in my head drift by. I was like a kid thumbing through his favorite deck of baseball cards and absorbed in them.

Brad raised his voice, "Terry, you must speak up. Talk to me and tell me what you see."

"My body is limp now. I'm still aware of others around me. They are aliens not people. The little grey ones are strong. An alien is always supervising. He watches the little ones and orders them around. I don't think the little ones are even alive. They're not living beings. They could be robots. They're having trouble with the laces on my boots… I know it's about to start!" I'm softly crying again.

"What's about to start, Terry?"

"The examination. They do medical things and hurt me while I'm on the table. I fill my lungs with air to scream and nothing comes out again. Oh God, help me please! There's a tall one there. Don't look at me. Oh, God he's going to look at me!"

Sensing my anxiety Brad squeezed my hand and said softly, "Relax now, Terry, and tell me about the tall one… he can't hurt you now. Tell me about him."

"He's not benign or malevolent. If he could talk, he'd say, 'Nothing personal, just doing my job, man.' He's a different type of entity, a different animal entirely. He's insect-like and as tall as the aliens. The grey ones are their drones to do his bidding and help him. They are worker bees."

"What does the insect thing want with you?" Brad asked.

"I think they are trying to learn our anatomy. Learn how we work. They show no empathy whatsoever and just go about their business. They hurt me with instruments and mechanical stainless-steel probes and knives. There are tools that hang from a low domed ceiling. Everything is white porcelain or stainless steel. I'm restrained, and they did medical things to me. I tried to tell them I wasn't anesthetized. I was less than a human being, I was their lab rat. Then they make me forget… and everything will be okay."

"Go on, Terry."

"If someone hurts you, Brad. If they hurt you and scare you but then make you forget it ever happened, does that make it okay? I think it's cruelty. These goddamn things are cruel! They hurt me, and I hate them all."

Brad asked, "Will they talk to you?"

"I try to talk to them every time. I want them to know I'm a living person aware of things and I can feel pain. They just ignore me. He was doing something to my chest, and it hurt like hell. I remember screaming and cursing. I think he became annoyed with my screaming."

"What makes you think you annoyed him?" Brad wanted to know.

"I heard his voice inside my head. I heard it as clearly as any spoken word. He told me I had to stop screaming. He said, 'You know us. We will not harm you. You will go back, and you will not remember, so why do you scream?' He touched my right temple again and I immediately lost consciousness until they took me back." I said.

I'm quiet again. My heart is still pounding. I'm watching various scenes play out in my head. So many things I didn't remember. These are the things the aliens made me forget.

Brad comforted me. There was a short pause. He squeezed my hand and told me, "You have done very well. But you must go back again to the tent. After they finish with you on the table what happens next? Just watch it in your mind, Terry. Tell me what you're seeing."

"We're back in the tent now. We were somehow placed on the ground near the car instead of back in the tent. Somebody screwed up. So, they had to carry us back. They put us back in the tent. Toby first, and then me. I was barely conscious. I remember a lot of pain. When they were satisfied with the way we were positioned, they left us. I lost consciousness as soon as they placed me on my air mattress."

"What happened next, Terry?"

"I woke up and saw Toby on his knees. He was staring out of the tent at something. I remember feeling confused when I woke up. We were both in a lot of pain. We watched them leave. Some of the little ones were still in the meadow and they had to walk into the beam."

"Terry, tell me what you saw when the little ones walked into the light."

"We watched them from the tent, they walked into the light and then dissolved into it. The ship rose up in the air like a hot air balloon. Then the corners changed color to all white."

"Good, that's very good." Brad paused for a moment. "Terry, this is very important. You enjoy photography, don't you?"

"Yes, Brad, I enjoy photography." I knew where this was headed. They think I took photographs of the spaceship and kept them secret. God, I wish I had. Again, I cursed myself for forgetting that camera. But who's to say it would have made a difference?

"You have a darkroom at home too, is that true?"

"Yes, Brad, I have a darkroom, but only for black and white pictures."

"Terry, have you ever taken pictures of the B52s or the nuclear sites? If you tell me, know we can fix things and you won't be in trouble."

I paused. I needed to concentrate, I remembered the photograph of Kilo-5 I took back in 1975, a couple months after the "black diamond" incident. I knew they didn't find it when they raided our home. The photograph itself wasn't a big deal but it would be hard to explain the "why." The launch facility was located off a state highway and visible to the public. I had blurted out so many things involuntarily. I was terrified of what I may have told Brad. My pause was too long for Brad's taste.

"Terry! Have you ever taken a picture at a site where photography is prohibited?"

I shot back without hesitation this time, "No, Brad!"

He seemed satisfied with my answer and moved along.

"Terry, did you tell agent Gregory the whole truth about your camping trip with Toby at Devil's Den? Did you tell the truth about your cameras and film?"

"Yes, Brad, Toby had a little camera and he never used it. Everything I told Gregory was the truth." I could sense we were almost finished. I was terrified by the thought of what they might do to me or how this might end. Brad had warned me that if I wasn't fully cooperative, "this could end badly."

"Terry, have you lied to me or to the agents about anything you saw or did while you were on your camping trip?"

"No, Brad." I had my wits about me again. The effects of the medicine must have been wearing off. I was careful not to betray my hypnotic posture.

I heard Brad ask the agents, "You boys good?"

Gregory spoke for the pair, "We're good, wrap it up, Brad," I also heard the captain say something funny and everyone laughed for a quick moment.

Brad then turned his attention back to me.

"You've done a very good job, Terry. Now, I'm going to make it all go away. Would you like that? You'll be at peace."

"Yes, Brad." I'm on autopilot again. I thought, No! No way will I forget this. Now, I knew what happened to me at Devil's Den. This was information I owned.

"Terry, in just a moment I'll take these ugly memories away forever. You will forget everything that happened to you at Devil's Den. You will forget that big ship and the aquariums, the men in tan uniforms with orange insignias. You will forget your trip to the moon, the things you saw, and the things you were told about the moon. You will forget everything that happened to you at Devil's Den and you will forget everything that happened to Toby. Ready?"

"Yes, Brad."

Brad resumed humming. He removed the adhesive bandage from my arm. I felt him swab my arm and I could smell rubbing alcohol. He cleaned up the injection site so there would be no trace. He carefully rolled down the sleeve of my shirt and rebuttoned it.

Brad said, "Listen, You and Toby went on a camping trip to Devil's Den and it was a horrible trip. You both were bug-bitten and sick, but that's all over now. When you recall what we did here today, all you will remember is our pleasant chat about camping, St Louis, and photography. UFOs and space people don't exist. There is nothing on the moon but rocks. The tiny woman who was kind to you, you will forget about her. She was just a dream. Everything you saw or heard at Devil's Den you will forget. It will be gone… and you won't be able to remember any of it, no matter how hard you try."

"Yes, Brad, I understand." Now, I am terrified.

"Now listen to my voice, Terry. Remember when we walked down those ten stairs and you turned on that light by pulling that chain? Remember, we turned on the light to look around?"

"Yes, Brad, I remember."

"We're all finished now. But before you can come back upstairs, you'll need to pull the chain to turn out that light. When you pull that chain and the light goes out, all those memories will be gone forever." He repeated himself once more, word for word. Then, "Terry, you won't be able to remember them no matter how hard you try. Ready?"

"Yes, Brad." What's really going to happen when I reach up and pull his imaginary chain? I reasoned that if Brad had control of my mind, he'd have control of my arm too. I also deduced, if my arm responds to Brad's command automatically, then I probably will forget everything. But, if I need to voluntarily reach up like I did when I turned it on, maybe I'll be able to keep some or all of what just occurred.

"Now, Terry. Now reach up and pull that chain and turn out that light. We're finished down here and it's time to come back upstairs. Now, reach up and grab that chain!"

Nothing happened. I waited to see if my arm would respond of its own volition. It didn't! I felt no compulsion to move my arm at all. I wanted to be certain that when I reached up and pulled that imaginary chain it would be my conscious act. The room was quiet. I didn't move. I knew Brad was growing anxious. I knew he'd repeat himself. I waited.

Then it came. Brad repeated his command, "Now, Terry, reach up and turn off that light."

This time I responded to Brad. I reached into the air like I did when we began. I mimicked pulling a faux chain. Then I let my arm slowly fall into my lap. I did a quick mental assessment.

There were gaps in the interrogation. But those were mostly early on when the medication's effect was at its strongest. I kept my memories and many new ones too. I knew we were close, but I knew we weren't finished. Not yet.

"Now, Terry, walk up those stairs with me. Here we go. With each step feeling more alert. Ten, nine, eight, feeling more awake now … four and feeling alert, three, two and one. Wake up, Terry. Open your eyes feeling rested and feeling great. Now take a big stretch."

Very consciously and deliberately, I opened my eyes, but I wasn't feeling great. I had been in that same position for hours, it felt good to stretch. It felt even better knowing this nightmare might finally end today. I noticed the agents were packing up their paperwork. There was a positive vibe in the room.

The major's little kit was under his arm. Without a word, he left the room. I know this will sound crazy and I don't know why but I expected a goodbye.

Briefcase in hand, Gregory said, "Finish out your enlistment and go to college, son. There's nothing on your record to worry about so long as you keep your mouth shut. You do understand the rules? You cannot talk about anything pertaining to your camping trip. That all ended here today. It's nobody's business. Am I getting through to you?"

"Yes, sir, I don't remember much about it anyway," I said, purely for Gregory's benefit.

Gregory was cordial, "Your old CO asked me to speak with you. The hospital's down a couple people. They could use you. But you'll be on day shift. Would you like to return to the hospital squadron?"

"Sir, I'd like to work as an EMT again. If I can go back, it would make me very happy, sir."

"Son, I'm not in the business of making people happy. Those orders will be cut this week. The driver will take you home. You can take the rest of the day off. I cleared it with your CO. Be careful what you photograph with that telescopic lens of yours."

"Yes, sir." With that, I was gone. He opened the door for me and left. I wanted to skip going down the hall like a ten-year-old. I was singing a song under my breath. One we used to sing in the schoolyard when I was about six or seven, "I know something you don't know, I know something you don't know."

They knew about the space people. The agents knew. They might even work for them or whoever is in their alien chain of command. I do know something they don't!

I recalled what Gregory told me when I called him that day and offered to take a polygraph test. He said he wasn't interested. He said, "I have my own lie detector, son." I think I just met his lie detector.

If the purpose of this exercise was to wipe my memory clean, they failed. They failed, and they don't even know it. Thanks to Brad, I know so much more. Now it made sense. Brad confirmed alien abduction, alien apathy, and alien amnesia. I'd had a dose of it all.

Those memories and the images that Brad's failed hypnotic session pulled into my conscious mind are mine now. I kept them too. They're tucked away in a little compartment inside my head. I knew I could keep them, most of them. What I didn't know was that they came with a heavy price.

Betty, the Lady MIB

Since the device in my leg was discovered back in 2012, memories of Devil's Den have returned to my conscious mind. I sometimes wonder how different my life would be had I not resisted Brad's promise to take those memories away. I may have missed the opportunity to surrender this madness into his hands.

I fought so hard to keep these memories because I own them, and I believed I could live with them. I was half-right. I learned early on that whenever I visit that night at Devil's Den, the horror of it all returns. Like I told Brad back in 1977, "These beings have rules," and I opted to stay in the game.

My wife and I have been programmed to avoid the topic. Like Pavlov's famous experiments with dogs, my wife and I are conditioned to avoid the topic because it causes us pain. We recognize the terror that always accompanies those memories. For forty years I had managed to keep the door to that compartment in my mind on lockdown.

The awareness of this object in my knee kicked down the door to that compartment. It's like the memories that come back to you when you page through your high school yearbook. You see people and things you hadn't thought about in years or maybe decades. Images you probably could never have recalled regardless of how hard you tried. You've heard the saying that, "something jogged my memory?" The right cue or trigger and the memories return. It works because memories never go away. They lie dormant, just underneath the skin like this thing in my leg.

Seeing the implants on film was the visual cue that triggered a response in my brain. Memories returned first as nightmares and eventually they seeped into my waking consciousness. Some things spontaneously returned to my awareness. Many came roaring back as horrific nightmares. The kind of nightmare you wake from screaming. This is not fantasy or hallucination. I recalled real events from the past. Everything that returned to my conscious memory dovetailed with what I could recall. Everything fits. Often, one dream would pick up where the previous dream ended.

Reviewing my notebooks brought back more terror and pain. The suffering was necessary to document everything. By journaling and writing I can both process these things and preserve them too. They are important. People need to know the truth. Alien entities are real, and we are all at risk of abduction or worse. Then there's the "agenda."

In late 2016, a new consequence came out of the darkness. I started to lose weight. The weight loss coincides with my decision to aggressively tell all that I know. Since I quit running in 2005, my weight went from my usual 190 lbs. to 240 lbs. and stayed. I carried an extra fifty pounds, but I was otherwise healthy. I'm now down to 150 lbs. It's a daily battle to keep my weight above 150 lbs. What concerns my doctor is what she refers to as a wasting of muscle. I'm now frail and vulnerable.

In 2013, I was duty-bound to find Tobias. Instinctually I knew Toby's testimony would bolster my own. I was far too late. He succumbed to alcoholism and the injuries he likely suffered at the hands of extraterrestrial beings and their co-conspirators.

That bucket of pills they sent home with us back in 1977 has always troubled me. I'm grateful for my wife's keen observation and her ability to make the connection between my sudden memory problems and the unmarked pills. Thanks to her, I only took them for three days and flushed the remaining eleven days down the toilet.

If Toby had taken all fourteen days as prescribed, what kind of effects could it have had on his psyche? I believe Toby also suffered worse treatment during the abduction. Like he said, "They hurt us, Terry." I could see the pain behind those bloodshot eyes. "Yeah, Tobe, they did hurt us." I believe Toby's obsession with the sky was a result of being abducted as a child. The loss of Toby's life made this project important on a personal level. It cost Toby the life he never had an opportunity to live. I want the world to know.

Although most of the past 40 or so years have been peaceful, I was still tagged. Like research animals in the wild, sometime in my past I'd been abducted and hopefully rendered unconscious while the ugly praying mantis creatures implanted their devices in my leg. How much of my life has been studied, monitored, and even manipulated by them?

My wife and a few trusted friends thought it would be wise to explore all possible explanations before labeling the metal device in my leg as paranormal. Friends pointed out that perhaps my films were accidentally switched in the emergency room. Maybe the X-rays I had belonged to someone else?

My wife and I knew that explanation wasn't possible. I discussed and viewed my X-rays at the hospital in real time. Instead of the routine two X-rays they took eight shots of my knee and asked a radiologist to view the films in my presence. These X-rays belong to me and are of no one else.

That left just one remote possibility. It's rare, but it's not paranormal.

We've all heard stories about combat veterans who 50 years after battle cough up a bullet. That fact was easy to verify. It really does happen on rare occasions. Is it possible that as a child, I swallowed this object? Could this thing, over 60 years have migrated from my digestive tract into my thigh just above my knee?

I had two possible explanations left. It was either a piece of metal I swallowed at some point in my life and it worked its way into my knee over the years. Or, it had been intentionally and covertly implanted in my knee using some method not recognized by modern medicine. Either by alien beings or maybe even by the USAF. I needed help from a medical professional. Fortunately, I knew someone.

The best candidate for my question was a friend back in Vermont. She's a board-certified radiologist who expressed interest in my knee; she asked that I protect her anonymity for the sake of her reputation in the medical community. I understand the stigma that goes with the topic. At her request, I'll refer to her as Dr. Hong.

She agreed to see me, and I paid the airfare for the flight to Burlington, Vermont. I showed her my 2012 X-rays and explained that there was no visible scar. I was totally candid with her. She understood the implications of what I was alleging. Before expressing her opinion, she insisted that she should examine my knee. After a thorough examination, she kindly explained.

"Mr. Lovelace, I'm not an expert in these matters. I don't know anyone who is. But I can't reconcile these X-rays and your knee. Could these X-rays belong to someone else?"

I explained that possibility had been ruled out at the VA Hospital. These X-rays belong to my knee.

"Whatever these artifacts might be, they were inserted into your thigh by methods unknown to medical science. It got inside your thigh without breaching the surface of your skin. There is absolutely zero probability that you swallowed an object that eventually worked its way to your leg. The digestive tract is a closed system.

I thanked her and paid her. Now, I am 100% certain by the weight of the evidence that during my life, a non-human entity implanted this object in my right knee. It could have been done any time prior to 2012. I think it's likely the cause of the "numb spot" that I experienced as a runner.

There is another fact worth mentioning. There are others with experiences nearly identical to mine. Our stories are incredibly similar. Every story I've researched regarding people who've been found to carry implants share two things common. First, they all claim to have experienced an abduction or other unique UFO interaction. Second, by chance they all discovered an object under their skin on X-ray without a corresponding scar.

Many credible people have stepped forward with unbelievable stories about alien abduction. But the world is little different today than it was when Betty and Barney Hill took that drive home through rural New Hampshire. In some small measure, I hope to change that.

Carl Sagan's observation was so true, "Extraordinary claims require extraordinary proof." Proof of alien contact that will stand up to the peer review process is just not going to happen until our government agrees to it. It's in their control or the control of their overlords.

If our government is sincere about its search for extraterrestrial life, why do they limit their search to listening for radio waves and searching for planets in distant galaxies? If they were genuinely interested in proof, why let thousands of police reports and witness statements rot in file cabinets across the country? As I said at the onset, our government wants the public to focus on far away galaxies. It's the events close to home that make them uncomfortable.

Why? I know three answers that make sense. In the law there are differing standards of proof to establish your assertion and win the case. Everyone knows to prove someone guilty of murder the standard of proof is beyond a reasonable doubt. In most civil matters the standard is to prove that your assertion is more likely than not, or sometimes referred to as, "51% vs. 49%". One standard of proof is by the weight of the evidence. The weight of the evidence over the past 60 years is more than enough to prove that extraterrestrial beings exist, and they visit our planet. A lot. They capture people and implant devices in them. It's an incredible claim but it's true and provable by the weight of the evidence.

If I were to take the case for extraterrestrial life visiting Earth to a trial by jury, I'm confident I could prove my case by the weight of the evidence.

So why does our government and governments globally turn a blind eye? I have three possible scenarios I'd ask you to consider: (1) There may be a quid pro quo arrangement. In exchange for technology we grant them permission to pursue their limited agenda without interference, or (2) Our government is working in concert shoulder to shoulder with alien beings toward a shared goal, or lastly (3) Our government is incapable of stopping alien beings from abducting people. In that case the government's role is to mitigate collateral damage and control public fear. Any one of these three scenarios are good reason to shift public attention to the search for distant planets and radio waves.

The topic of alien implants is the butt of jokes and fodder for comedians. But devices implanted in people are sometimes recovered. I'm not unique. Alien implants have been discovered by happenstance like mine. A few were surgically recovered for laboratory analysis.

A podiatrist from California named Dr. Roger Leir recovered several from men and women until his death in 2014. He was a brave man and suffered ridicule in the medical community. All his patients claimed to have been a victim of alien abduction or had experienced lost time. When Leir recovered implants, they were analyzed and found to be composed of exotic material. Some of the metals were found to exist on Earth only in meteorites. Some were of hitherto unknown elements that will remain unknown because they were never shared within the scientific community.

In early 2016, I began gathering drawings and journals from 1977 forward. Sheila too, had chronicled occurrences between 1977 through 1987 in diaries of her own. Fortunately, she had the forethought to safely store everything that we'd chronicled. In our storage locker she found the sketches I drew in 1977 through 1979 that we both thought had been lost.

The nightmares began in early 2013 after the discovery of the implants. They began in earnest immediately after I made a public appearance at a September 2017 UFO conference in Houston. The real consequence would come a month later. It would be epic.

It arrived on a Friday evening. My wife and I went out for dinner and saw a movie. I don't recall what we watched but it wasn't anything in the horror or science fiction genre. It was a pleasant evening and we were home by around 11:00 PM.

I performed my usual nighttime ritual of locking things up and setting the alarm. I made it to bed a little before midnight and fell soundly asleep for what felt like just an instant.

When I opened my eyes, I found myself in our family room! I was seated upright in my chair and sweating profusely. I could see the alarm panel from my chair. The alarm was set and had not been triggered. Never in my life have I walked in my sleep. Not once.

Seated directly across from me is what I first mistook to be a small Asian woman. I would estimate her height at four feet. She wore oversized sunglasses that hid her large almond eyes and part of her face. She wore a red headscarf she had loosely tied to hide her pencil thin neck. Aside from the red scarf, she was dressed all in black. Black blouse buttoned to the top with long sleeves that partially hid the four very long digits. Her pants and shoes were also black. She sat casually with a non-threatening posture.

My first thought was the "men in black" or the MIB who supposedly confronted people who've had UFO experiences. Their alleged goal is to dissuade witnesses from telling others about their experience. Honestly, I thought the MIB stories were urban legend and just a movie plot. But even urban legends sometimes have a kernel of truth.

I felt mildly sedated. The house was silent except for my breathing. I caught that strange ionized scent in the air and the hair on my arms stood up. I thought to call out for my wife, but I knew she wouldn't wake up. They make sure of that too.

I recalled that in 1987, my wife woke up to find a tiny woman standing at the edge of our bed. She spoke telepathically and told her, "Everything is okay, go back to sleep." An entity, possibly the same entity, now sitting across from me may have visited our home in 1987 and never tripped the alarm or disturbed the dog. I guess I shouldn't be surprised to find her in my home a second time.

She wore a wig. It was an outdated style with jet-black hair sitting slightly askew on top of her head. From a silhouette her hair reminded me of the cartoon character from the *Flintstone*s cartoons of the 60s, "Betty Rubble." I couldn't help but think, "That wig looks ridiculous."

She immediately replied, telepathically. I heard her clearly inside my skull and her voice was familiar.

"So, you don't like my hair? It's the same."

"The same as what?" I thought.

"The same as the last time we met."

I heard her, but her lips never moved. I'd forgotten. They communicate telepathically. That was their method of communication. My unspoken comment had hurt her feelings.

"No, no I'm just shocked and scared... that's all, scared." I felt compelled to add, "It looks very nice."

She seemed to acknowledge my apology.

This was beyond surreal. I was in my own home sitting across from a half human and half alien being while my wife slept just down the hallway. This was the same being I encountered a long time ago. That didn't change the fact that I was scared out of my wits. I hoped to escape without being abducted again and subjected to another one of their torturous examinations.

Then it registered. It struck me like a bolt of lightning. That 1987 motorcycle ride when I lost two hours of time. They abducted me from that gravel farm road. Ten years earlier at Devil's Den, I was taken for the umpteenth time with poor Toby along for the ride. I remembered, or should I say they allowed me to remember those things. I was certain I met her during that abduction and probably a long time before that.

The voice I heard in my head came as plainly as a spoken word. She spoke with perfect English grammar with no discernable accent. She responded to my thoughts immediately, "Yes, I'm *that* woman. No, you will not be taken tonight. No more examinations, ever. I promise."

Her promise ebbed my fear by a degree. Very soon all my fears had vanished. I wasn't surprised.

I stared at her and recognized her face. I recognized her voice too. I was amazed that she hadn't aged since I last saw her in 1987. Her body shape and facial structure were identical to the woman I met in 1987. As I stared at her, I picked up more human features in her face. She impressed me as a hybrid being made up of one-half human and one-half alien. I assume that's true because she didn't correct me.

She was aware that I was still trying to deal with her appearance. I wanted to see more of her face.

She removed her sunglasses and revealed her large almond shaped eyes. They were black and not as large as what they portray in the exaggerated pictures in the media. Despite the familiarity, I was shocked by her appearance. She was not a human being. She was something else and that was disturbing.

My mind raced. Why is this woman in my home? Did she intend to harm me because I spoke openly about my experiences?

Of course, she intercepted those thoughts and reassured me she would not harm me. But she stated that my public disclosures and writing a book for publication was worrisome to both her hosts and to my government.

She knew what I was thinking. It was hard to process. I remember in elementary school; a teacher once asked the class to not think about elephants. Of course, everyone could think of nothing but elephants. Controlling our own thoughts is not as easy as it sounds. I was afraid a wrong thought could have terrible consequences.

For that reason, I thought it was important to address the issue of privacy. Directing my thought toward her, I registered my concern, "I'm accustomed to my thoughts being private and not open for others to know unless I choose to do so. Some thoughts are my own and I may not wish to share them with others."

She replied as I finished the sentence. "Yes, you can have privacy. You can keep some of your thoughts private, Terry. Just try."

I was moved by the fact she used my name. But I was unsure if she was telling me the truth or just placating me. It was evident that she didn't require time to compose her thoughts. Every time, her reply immediately followed my last word.

She added, "You already know how to keep things separated in your mind. You already know how to keep some thoughts private. You can do so if you wish to."

"I'll try."

"Terry, I am here because you have memories that cannot be permanently suppressed or removed safely from your mind. Because those memories cannot be erased, you intend to tell others to help you manage these unwelcome thoughts. By telling others you hope to confirm your experiences and make people aware."

"I agree. But what could I know that is so important? Lots of people write books and openly discuss their experiences. Why am I singled out?"

She was unequivocal, "You know things and you have seen images of things that are crucial to their shared agenda. They are important to both your government and to my hosts. You are not aware of their importance and you can't discern which memories are sensitive and should not be disclosed. To remove them now would cause you great harm."

It was difficult to stay on topic. I asked, "Is this thing in my leg tied to all of this? How many people have been tagged with an implant like mine?" I wanted to know but I wasn't prepared for the answer.

"Many, many thousands over three generations," was her reply.

I was stunned by her answer. I asked her, "Please answer two questions for me. What is the purpose of this thing in my leg? Are you here to persuade me to not disclose what I know?"

Her answers continued to astonish me, "You have devices in both of your legs. They serve a purpose and they have caused you no harm. If you continue to speak publicly and if you publish your book, my hosts will recover them. That is the limit of my hosts' concern."

Then it occurred to me. My left leg had never been X-rayed. I have two of these things inside of me! My next thought was, "Why… how can the devices be removed?"

"My hosts will not allow you to have them removed here and analyzed by terrestrial scientist for their composition. They won't harm you and you'll experience no pain. They'll remove them from your body while you're sleeping. Your government also has interests in you and in your devices," she added.

I asked, "I still don't understand. Can you answer plainly? These things in my leg, what purpose do they serve?"

"The devices have many purposes. The concern among all is that once disclosed they will support your claims. Your government will not allow it. They will first attempt to discredit you," she said with emphasis.

"Who are your hosts?" I asked. It seemed like such an odd way to refer to whatever entities she worked for. "Host" can be a verb as in to "host" a dinner party. It can also be used to reference a symbiotic relationship that can be mutualistic or parasitic.

She gave an eloquent reply, "You call them aliens. I refer to them as my hosts because they are not alien to me."

With that question answered, I asked again, "A lot of people write books, speak in public and in the media on the topic of extraterrestrial beings visiting Earth. Why would my government not allow me to disclose these things? Why is my information any different?"

She didn't reply but nodded her head.

What happened next was a graphic replay of four scenes from my past. I could see four vignettes play out in my mind's eye. Each scene was a concise episode of a life event. It played out in color graphics and the quotes spoken in my own voice. I was outside myself as an observer from behind and above.

It was very much like the images Major Brownfield a/k/a Brad pulled up and into my conscious memory under my semi-hypnosis session. These were not my thoughts and I could not control what was happening in each scene. Each scene lasted only 60 or so seconds. I was amazed at how much she could convey in just a few short minutes.

In the first scene, I was seated in the interrogation room at the OSI building on Whiteman AFB back in 1977. I watched myself telling Brad about the ship's dimensions and its interior. I told him that it was so huge it could never fly across the side of the moon that faces the Earth.

Then a very disturbing memory. One I hadn't remembered in decades. There were other humans inside that ship. Not captives like us. They were humans; the men wore military haircuts and were around my age. they wore tan uniforms with red or orange insignias. They ignored us completely and went about their business. It was plain to see they were members of the ship's crew in some capacity.

Then I recalled the commotion in the interrogation room when I made that revelation. Brad was quick to instruct me, "Terry, you will forget about them now. You'll not remember them, understand?"

"Yes Brad, I understand."

Next, I saw myself seated at my kitchen table drawing pictures of the large ship.

In the second vignette I saw myself inside the very large ship. There's a petite woman by my side and we were talking, exchanging thoughts. I held my motorcycle helmet in my right hand by its strap. It is the same woman sitting across from me. We are looking through a giant window at a jet-black sky with a billion stars. It was breathtaking. I felt we must be in a large warehouse of some kind. I never experienced the slightest sensation of motion. Then from the right side of the panel the moon rolled into my view. It was huge. We were no more than 30,000 feet above it I'd later estimate. At that moment, I thought, "It's going to hit us!" Betty then assured me telepathically we were the ones moving, not the moon. She explained we were onboard a ship and all was well.

The sliver of moon I saw in front of us was the edge of the bright side, glowing greyish-white. The ship turned, and we traveled into the dark side. We travelled some distance and everything in front of us was black. The stars were no longer visible. There was only darkness. This was the dark side of the moon and we had turned to face the surface. Soon, I saw specks of light on the surface below us. There were more and more lights spread across the darkened landscape. We were closer, and buildings were clearly visible. It was an entire city. It was a huge sprawling complex. It was akin to the view from a commercial airliner on a landing approach over LAX at night. The randomness of the buildings was confusing for a moment. Something looked out of place. Then it struck me, the city looked odd because there were no roads or streets. There were no parking lots or vehicles. Just a large collection of randomly scattered structures. Many of the buildings had square windows and the interiors were well lit.

I was fascinated by the view below. She said the ship we were in was too large to land on the moon. She told me there were human beings living and working on the moon. In this vignette our dialogue in 1987 went as follows.

I asked, "Human beings are living here? How long have we been here?"

"For many decades," she said matter-of-factly. She said they were, "There to collect and process the rocks."

This ended vignettes one and two. These are the two things she warned me not to disclose for my safety. The third I've explained as relevant only between my wife and me. Whatever importance there may be in that fourth scene is above my level of understanding.

I have shared the content of Betty's warning with my wife and editor, but no one else. The information will be released if I abruptly die or meet some unfortunate end. I thought it was prudent to do so considering my health.

She gave me just those four "chapters" presented without commentary and received by me as a gift. I'm certain these were not random thoughts, dreams, or hallucinations. These came directly from her mind to mine. I believe this was her way to tell me not to publish. Further, not to openly discuss alien visitation, alien hybrids, and human involvement openly. I believe the sensitive information concerns humans living on the moon, the "big ship" and the collecting and processing of rocks. That's all she shared.

The questions I asked her were rarely the ones I would have chosen if I'd been given time to think through what she said before composing my next question.

She then said words that still haunt me, "Your government will kill you."

I should have asked so much more but I was numb. In the minute or two it took me to regain my composure, the scene went to black.

I woke up in the living room chair at dawn. I walked to my office and recorded as much as I could remember. Then I went back to bed and slept soundly until noon.

I do my best to not dwell on what she told me. It would be too easy to obsess. I go about my daily activity and choke the memories down. I read the news and wonder where our civilization is headed. I write and publish my book, so others will know this stuff is real. Our government, world governments, have kept us in the dark far too long.

I am writing a second book. My wife suggested writing 40+ years ago to cope with the alien interactions in my life. It was helpful for me back then. It is helpful for me today.

The words, "If you tell … they will kill you," worry me some, but not enough to deter my efforts. I feel the more exposure I have the safer I am.

After her appearance, I went to work with a newfound urgency. It was more important than ever to record everything I knew. And make it accessible to the public.

There's no way I'll ever know how much was hidden from me. Betty was very clear about a couple things. Her claim that the devices I carry in both legs would be removed by her hosts. Less than a month later they came calling and retrieved their property while I slept.

I woke up on November 16, 2017 with pain in both of my legs between my knee and my groin. Twenty-four hours later the bruises began to appear and the pain in my legs made walking painful. With help from my wife, we photographed my legs. The wound in the center of the bruising looked like insect bites. When photographed and enlarged they were box shaped clearly distinguishable from an insect bite. From what I know about human anatomy, nothing in the human body has 45-degree angles and straight lines.

On the morning of November 18th, I set out to get my legs X-rayed. That proved to be more difficult than I ever imagined. Hospital X-ray facilities require an order from a staff physician. My physician friends were spread out between Michigan, Vermont, and American Samoa. Free-standing imaging centers not associated with a hospital likewise require a doctor's order.

On a long shot I stopped by a chiropractic office without an appointment. After a 45-minute wait he offered to speak to me. He was initially disinterested. Then he glanced at the X-ray I held up to his face as he was escorting me to the door. He stopped dead in his tracks. Staring at the X-ray for a minute or so he invited me into his office and asked me to tell him the condensed story. I did, and he listened. He listened for 45 minutes despite his phone ringing and urgent knocks on his office door.

He wrote a prescription for an X-ray and told me where to go. No payment required but he did ask to see a copy of the films.

Two hours later I was home and holding the X-ray film up to the sunlight pouring through my kitchen window. Neither my wife nor I have enough knowledge to evaluate an X-ray, but it was clear the metal things were missing. On both sides of my legs they appeared to be gone. We found what Betty promised. Her hosts had reclaimed their property. They were gone. At least the metallic ones above the knee were gone.

Betty's hosts had visited me in the middle of the night and removed both devices from my upper legs. I guess I wasn't prepared for that. I should have been. She said they would remove them and attempt to discredit me.

In the morning, I dropped the X-rays off for the chiropractor to see. He was busy with patients, so I left them at the front desk. I still didn't know where this development left me.

At five o'clock that evening my chiropractor friend called on my cell. "Well," he asked, "what do you think of your films?" I explained I didn't know whether to be elated or depressed.

He was upbeat, "The metallic objects are mostly gone from both legs. But the anomalies below the knee are still intact without change."

"Whoa, doctor. What exactly do you mean when you say they are *mostly gone*? The implants are gone from both legs... but they failed to remove something?!"

"They did indeed. There are two tiny fragments of wire left behind. They are tiny, but they are plain to see. If you know where to look."

I couldn't believe it! He told me where to look and I was thrilled. There they were! Two tiny wires, side by side.

They had left something behind. It was my validation as much as a curtain tucked into the venetian blinds. I now had the proof I hoped for. I was wise to document the wounds on my legs. Those two pieces of wire left behind are the evidence to prove my case. Extraordinary claims require extraordinary proof. I have extraordinary proof in my right leg. Above and below my knee

I thanked my chiropractor friend and he declined payment. But he asked for a copy of my book. Of course, I promised him a copy.

I valued an opinion from a chiropractor; they look at dozens of X-rays daily. But I need solid confirmation from a board-certified radiologist. I bought a ticket to Burlington to see my friend Dr. Hong one more time. She was perfect because she had seen my "before" films. Now she'd see the "after."

Placing the new film on her light box, she studied them for a moment. She was shocked to see the metallic object she documented earlier, was gone. This time she was looking for a scar where the metal devices had been removed. Faint bruises were still visible on my upper thigh. The small box-like wounds from the center of both petal-like patterns of bruising were still visible. They had mostly healed by then but were still somewhat squarely shaped.

Next, she turned her attention to the lower and lateral area of my right thigh. She looked for any signs of an incision that would be left had the object had been surgically removed. Of course, there was none. Next, because the wires are so tiny, she wanted to rule out intentional deception.

Apologetically, she explained, "If you implanted these yourself, or if someone else did it for you, a puncture wound would still be visible. I know where to look for evidence of a puncture that would correspond to the placement of the wires." Her examination of my legs took ten minutes.

There was no sign of a wound or puncture site anywhere on my thigh. After comparing both X-ray images closely, she said, "These are not film anomalies. These are consistent with the object in the original X-ray. It's my medical opinion that the metallic structure I saw in your 2012 X-ray is now gone. Further, there's no trace of a surgical incision to explain its removal. In its place now are two, tiny lengths of wire in deep muscle tissue in the right thigh. The round artifacts below the knee are unchanged. Mr. Lovelace, you have a very unusual knee."

"Yes, doctor. I've been told that before."

Betty and Barney Hill's famous interrupted ride through New Hampshire didn't change things. When I lived in Vermont, I'd travel that same stretch of road where the Hills were taken aboard a spaceship. But never at night. I did so probably once a year in silent reflection. I'm hopeful there will come change and disclosure very soon. More credible people in government positions like Mr. Hellyer will step up and risk ridicule or worse to disclose the truth.

This is the way things stand as of 2018. I believe mankind has made some incredible discoveries they've managed to keep secret. Little by little we all work to reach that tipping point.

EPILOGUE

The question on everyone's mind is, "When can we expect disclosure from our government?" Never. The answer is never.

Oh, it's coming. But it'll manifest through a grassroots movement. You're a party to it already. *We are disclosure* my friends. Think, talk, read, argue, and share. I know some of you will say, "If I can't see it with my own two eyes ..." That's okay. I'm not here to change your mind. I'm here to open your eyes. If you can just say, "There might be something to all this," that's enough! I understand. We've all been programed to deny, deny, deny...

If some of this resonates with you on a deeper level, I encourage you to be introspective. If you're struggling with intrusive thoughts, nightmares or worse, please, reach out to someone. Reach out to me. I'm not a therapist but if you'd like to share privately, I'll listen to you, reply, and help if I can. Visit www.terrylovelace.com or you can securely contact me at abducted in 1977@yahoo.com. I will respect your anonymity.

THE END

•••

OPUS

The Organization for Paranormal Understanding and Support

The sometimes disturbing, difficult to believe or spiritual nature of anomalous experiences might lead an individual to seek professional help, but because these experiences often fall outside the realm of what is considered "normal", there is often a lack of professionals willing or able to work with these issues. OPUS has recognized the need for a clearinghouse where an experiencer can receive assistance in locating and choosing a professional who is knowledgeable about a particular experience in question.

When appropriate, OPUS refers experiencers to physicians, licensed mental health practitioners, consultants, investigators and alternative health assistants. OPUS also refers to support groups of all kinds where experiencers can share feelings and concerns without fear of ridicule or embarrassment, while learning to understand, bridge and integrate what happened to them into daily life.

Recently, in addition to our face to face support group, OPUS has created an international "on-line" support group which can only be accessed by the members and is available 24/7. For UFO matters, OPUS networks with many like-minded groups and organizations such as Yvonne Smith and CERO (Close Encounter Research Organization), Dr. Leo Sprinkle and ACCET (Academy of Clinical Close Encounters Therapists, Inc), Barbara Lamb, MS, and previously with the late Dr. John Mack (JEMI) and Budd Hopkins (Intruder Foundation). For psychic issues, we refer to Loyd Auerbach of the Paranormal Network and for Kundalini, to the Kundalini Support Network and Kundalini Awakening Now. For spiritual emergencies, we refer to June Steiner PhD and the Spiritual Emergence Network.

Co-founded in 1994 by Les Velez and Dr. Eugene Lipson we seek to understand and support people having paranormal experiences.

In recent years the level of consciousness with regard to paranormal phenomenon has been growing. Increasing numbers of people are identifying experiences regarded as anomalous and most are without explanation. This leads not only to questions but also to a need for further support of some kind. This support should be based on the individual's experience and reaction to the phenomenon. This is why OPUS has been organized; OPUS...The Organization for Paranormal Understanding and Support.

The mission of OPUS is to educate and support people having unusual /anomalous personal experiences. Such experiences may include extraordinary states of consciousness, spiritual or parapsychological phenomenon, close encounters with non-human entities, and / or UFO activity.

OPUS, through its educational services and position of neutrality, provides a safe and caring meeting place for people and groups with the intention of working together to further our overall knowledge in these areas and better support people to integrate their anomalous experiences into everyday life. You can read more about this on our Experiencer Support page.

OPUS is a non-profit tax-exempt corporation formed for the public good and is recognized by the I.R.S. under section 501(c) 3. Its activities are guided by an executive council around which is created the larger network of volunteers, mental and medical practitioners, and experts in various fields. Please contribute whatever you can by sending your tax-deductible check to the mail address listed and donate through PayPal. Volunteers are welcome and encouraged to participate.

OPUS can be found at (http://opusnetwork.org) where the website provides information on clinical discussions and contact information. Our snail mail address 2701 I Street, Sacramento California 95816.

Photos

The author awaiting assignment to Whiteman Airforce Base 1973

Polaroid of Kilo-5 missile silo taken a few months after the sighting of the "black diamond" 1975

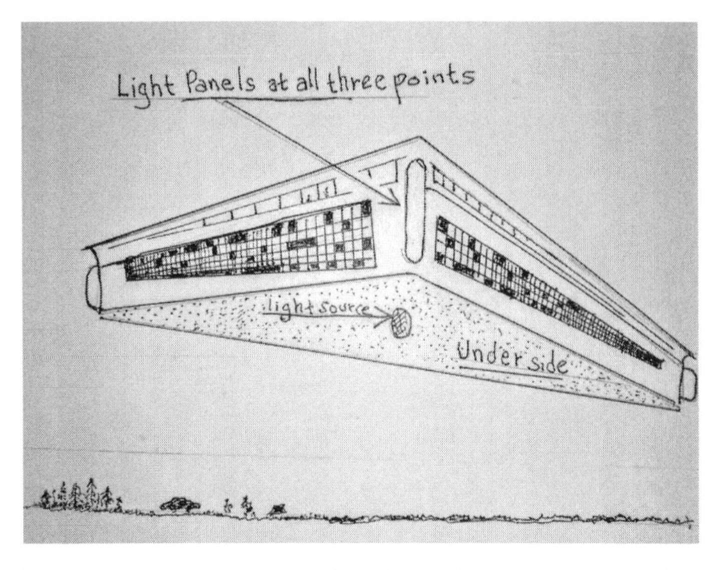

Redrawn by author from a sketch dated September 4th, 1977
Note: people, car, and tent shown for scale

Author drawn scene as viewed from a rear window of his home in August of 1978

Radiograph of author's thigh 2012

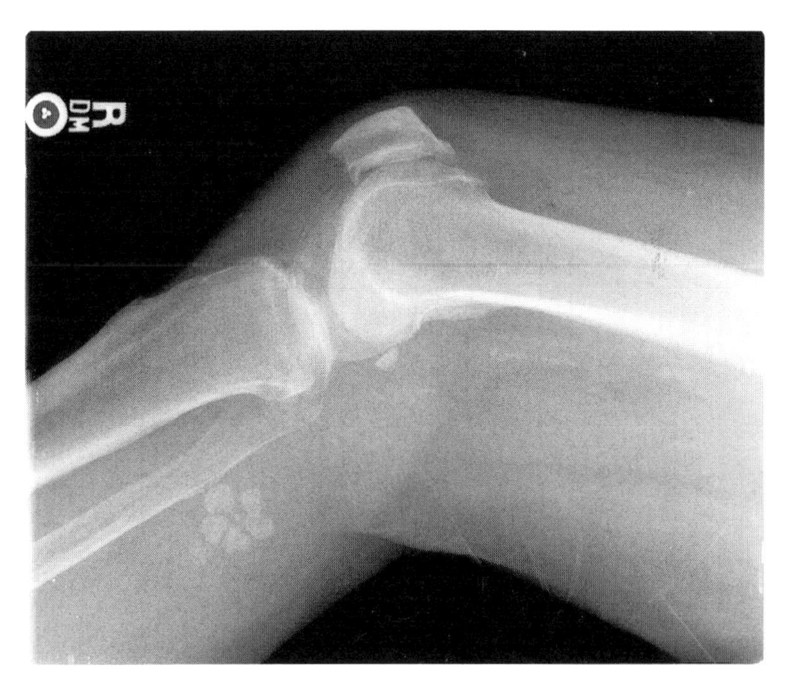

Radiograph of author's calf 2012

"Betty" the lady MIB drawn immediately following her visit October 2017

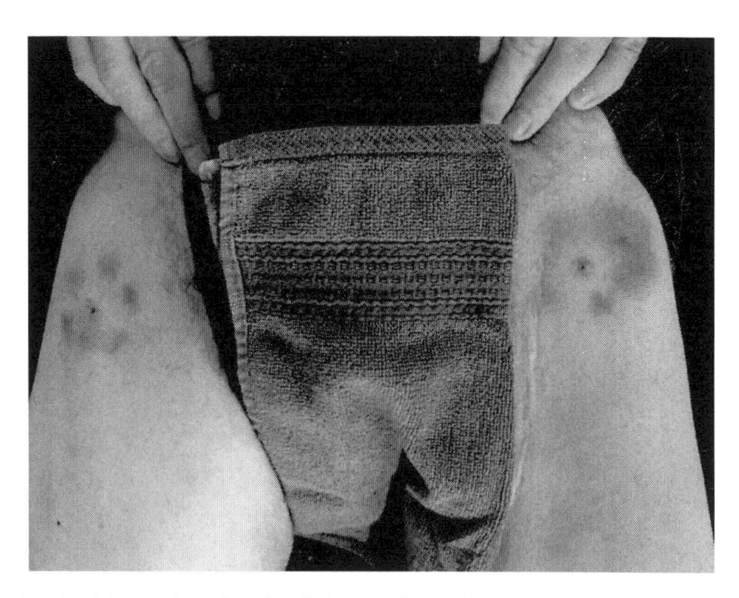

Author's thighs showing bruising and small square hole where metal anomaly was removed as "Betty" had promised less than a month previous November 16, 2017

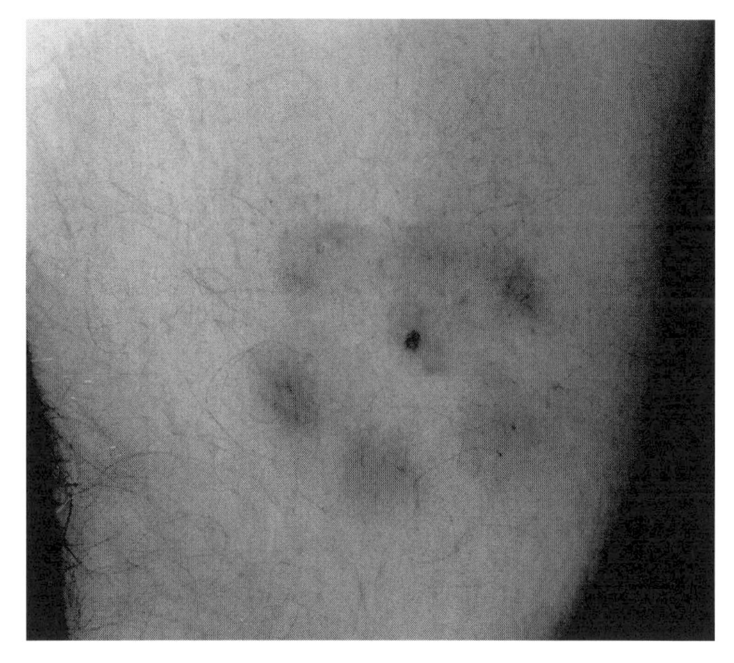

Close up of thigh bruises and square hole November 16, 2017

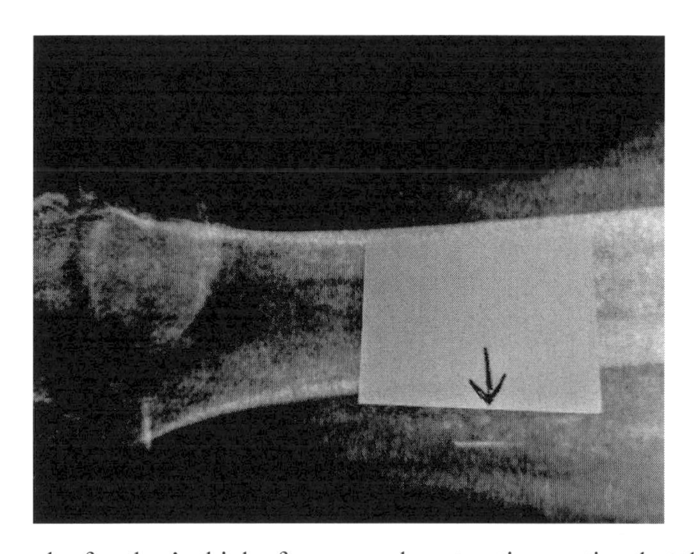

Radiograph of author's thigh after anomaly extraction, notice that the thin wire was left, but the square metal piece is gone November 16, 2017

Author as Assistant Attorney General of US Samoa Territory 2005

Author Terry Lovelace today as he works to keep his weight above 150 lbs. since his inexplicable and dramatic weight loss of nearly 80 lbs. over a 2-year period 2018